The Complete Anti-Inflammatory Diet & Action Plans for Beginners

350 Recipes and 10-Week Meal Plans to Boost the Immune System and Restore Overall Health

Rene Scott

Table of Contents

Introduction

When you are fighting inflammation, you know it is a real fight. There is going on in your body and mind that it can be overwhelming and often exhausting. There is a reason for fatigue as a symptom of inflammation, after all! Throughout this guide and your research, you will encounter various tips and techniques for helping you embrace the anti-inflammatory lifestyle and live a healthier life, but even that can be overwhelming. One of the essential tips you can ever receive when in this fight is to create your action plan.

It means you need to do more than say out loud that you will start focusing on your health and reducing the impact of chronic inflammation in your life. It is looking at how you are going to implement it in your life. It includes developing a statement that is specific and actionable. One example is addressing your water consumption. You cannot just say you are going to drink more water every day. It would be best if you determined how much and how you will drink more water every day. Use this simple water example to help develop an actionable and realistic plan using the steps below:

Identify what you are currently doing and be honest! For the water example, how much water do you currently drink? Do not try to be "good" during your observational period; be real. How much do you average throughout a few days? Being honest helps you create a baseline that you will build on. If you cheat and try to do more than you usually do during this time, you will only set yourself up for failure. Instead, do what you usually do and start from there.

What do you want to be doing that you can accomplish? It is stating the exact thing you want to improve. You do not say here, "drink more water." You say something like, "Increase the amount of water I drink each day from five cups to eight." Or "Drink at least nine cups of water per day." Be specific and realistic when defining your goal.

How do you achieve this goal? Are you going to set the alarm to remind you to drink a cup or two of water? Or do you want a new water bottle that you can fill with your daily amount of water that you can drink on within the day, making sure it is empty by the time you go to bed? You need to specify how you plan on keeping track of how you are achieving your goal and what you are going to use to help you get there. It may change as you start working towards your goal, but the idea is specific about what you want to try. For example, if you find a big water bottle is unrealistic for you to carry around all day, maybe you find a smaller water bottle that you know you need to fill up three times throughout the day, so you set the alarm to remind you to finish and refill during the day. It means you change the "how" portion of your plan, but not the goal.

Keep your eye on the small, achievable actions you can take to reach your larger health goals. Apply this formula to the changes you plan to make while following the anti-inflammatory diet. Think about how you would approach your fruit and vegetable consumption or the inclusion of fish per week. Address how you plan to cut out sugars and saturated fats or handle special occasions and the temptations that are sure to present themselves. Do not overwhelm yourself with a million different action plans, but rather select a couple to focus on and keep adding to your healthy focus as you develop new anti-inflammatory habits.

Remember, this is your life and your relationship with food. All of us are different, and your body may respond to foods differently than someone else. It means that your plan may not look like another's, and that is ok! Select a change that you want to make, and work your way into your personalized plan. Once you find a difference and "how" that works for your life and needs, move on to your steps. Below are some different changes you can choose from that will help you with adopting the anti-inflammatory diet. Some are "Do's," while others are "Do not."

The "Complete" Anti-Inflammatory Diet Plan

Remove the junk foods and processed foods from your kitchen, pantry, work drawers, and life. Keep tabs on the ingredient labels for anything that comes pre-packaged to make sure what you are eating is actually healthy and not just junk food in disguise.

Stick to whole foods when you can. You may not always choose real food because life is busy and hectic, but plan when this may or will happen. For example, instead of buying a pastry and a fancy coffee on your way to work in the morning, prep something that will support your healthy living the night before so you can still grab-and-go but without the negative health consequences (and added expense!).

Increase the amount of fruit you eat every day. It can be fresh, canned, or frozen, but if it is not fresh, make sure there is no added sugar or ingredients. Fruit juice does not count because it loses a lot of the necessary nutrients whole versions contain.

Eat more vegetables every day. These can also be fresh, canned, or frozen like the fruits. They also should not have any added sugars or ingredients if they are packaged. Some people do not like the taste of vegetables. That is ok! Try to get some in daily in a minimally processed way. Find a few that you can eat often, and if necessary, get a couple of servings in through soups, smoothies, or juice.

Focus on whole grains for each meal. Sometimes rice and whole-wheat toast can get a little "old" for your taste buds. There are many choices out there that it can be fun to experiment a little. Look for some different store options like wild rice, couscous, Teff, Kamut, quinoa, buckwheat, faro, and millet. Make it a fun challenge to find other ways to prepare these various ingredients.

Eat oily, cold-water fish twice per week. Look for fish that are wild-caught or sustainably sourced.

Increase your intake of additional protein or omega-3 fatty acid sources, including chia seeds, flax seeds, hemp seeds, edamame, or walnuts.

Cut back on your caffeine consumption to two cups per day. A cup is equal to eight ounces.

When drinking something other than water, choose teas like rooibos, white or green, or black coffee.

Carry a snack bag of mixed, raw, whole nuts and seeds to snack on throughout the day.

Snack on olives throughout the day to make sure you get plenty of "good" fat in your diet.

Swap out your cooking oils for either avocado oil or extra virgin olive oil.

Cut out foods that contain any refined sugar that is added to it. The nutrition label provides this information to determine if the sugar in the item is from added refined sugar sources or natural sweeteners. The ingredient list is currently necessary for this information, but soon it will be easily distinguished on the label under the "sugar" line.

Cut back on trans-fats. There are key terms in the ingredient list of packaged foods that are "red flags," and you need to avoid that food. For example, avoid anything that says, "partially hydrogenated oil," or "hydrogenated oil."

Increase your physical activity. It may mean that you get up and take a walk around your floor a couple of times a day, or park further away from your front door. Find ways to sneak in more physical activity during your day, even in small spurts.

Sleep plenty every night. Try to develop a good night time routine that helps you fall asleep and stay asleep for seven to nine hours. And make it quality sleep if you can! It helps you function better the following day and allows your body to restore itself throughout the evening. Just one night of lost hours of sleep can inflame your cells and start damaging your tissue. Create a plan to help you avoid this at all costs.

Focus on reducing constant stress in your life every day. Things like deep breathing or meditation are excellent tools to help you calm your body down and deal with stress. Stress can harm your body and mind, especially if it is chronic stress. It would be best to create a plan to deal with the stresses of daily life and the big things that can derail all your hard work.

How to Start and Maintain Your Plan

Again, the best way to implement this anti-inflammatory diet plan is to tackle one item at a time with a realistic set of steps. It is a gradual process that can help you move into this lifestyle with confidence and success. This incremental approach is what will make your plan start with success and continue it for the long-term. Each time you make an empowered, sustainable step forward, you keep moving down your path to an anti-inflamed, healthy, and happy life. Some people may adopt this plan in a few weeks, while others may take more than six months to develop a full schedule for themselves. Do not focus on what someone else is doing, but rather on what will work for you.

And just because you do not see an immediate change does not mean it is not working. Each positive choice you make compounds with the other positive choice you continue to make, setting off a ripple of healing and supportive actions inside your body. You may not notice them yet, but you must trust that they are working in your favor. Eventually, you will see a trimmer waist or experience more energy or even enjoy minimizing illnesses when you make it your lifestyle!

CHAPTER 1:

What is It?

The anti-inflammatory diet is not just for weight loss, although you may lose weight while on this diet. It is not a limited, three-week trek to push current inflammation from the body. It is not a false, quick leap to health. It provides a specific, new approach to your life: a way of life complete with all the nutrients and minerals, calories, and proteins that one needs to live well and happily. The anti-inflammatory diet components will help boost your overall health by providing the necessary nutrients and inflammation-fighting compounds to allow your body to heal itself and maintain proper balance. You will begin to notice changes in how you look and feel. You will have a sense of renewed energy. Your skin will take on an unmistakable healthy glow. Your body will be working correctly, producing new healthy cells, and calming the chaos of inflammation within your system. To follow the anti-inflammatory diet and reap the health benefits, you must understand yourself.

Symptoms of Inflammation

The main signs of inflammation include; heat, redness, pain, swelling, and muscle-function loss. These symptoms depend on the inflamed body part and its cause. Some of the widespread signs of chronic inflammation are:

- Frequent infections
- Weight gain.
- Body pain.
- Insomnia
- Fatigue
- Mood disorders like anxiety and depression
- Gastrointestinal problems like diarrhea, constipation, and acid reflux disease.

The typical symptoms of inflammation rely on various inflammatory effect problems. When the body defends mechanism which influences the skin, it causes rashes. When you are dealing with arthritis rheumatoid, it affects the joints. Most of the signs and symptoms experienced are fatigue, tingling, joint pains, stiffness, and swelling.

Similarly, when experiencing inflammatory bowel, it typically influences the digestive system. Its usual signs consist of bleeding ulcers, anemia, weight loss, bloating, pains, diarrhea, and stomach pains. With multiple sclerosis, the condition occurs on the myelin sheath, which covers the nerve cells. Its signs consist of problems when passing out stool, double vision, blurred eyesight, fatigue, and cognitive issues.

If you encounter any of the symptoms and the health problems, you could be suffering from inflammation. Many people link it to joint pains like arthritis, which can be signaled by swelling and aches. The problem is related to health problems, not just swollen joints. Nevertheless, all soreness is not bad. For instance, acute inflammation is vital throughout recovery from a twisted and puffy ankle.

It is easy to detect Chronic inflammation signs and causes. Insomnia, genetic predisposition, your food intake, and other individual habits can cause it. Similarly, inflammation resulting from allergic may also develop in your gut.

Below are some of the possibilities that you may be having it:

- If you always feel tired to the extent of not having enough sleep, not getting enough nap, or sleeping excessively.
- Do you experience time-to-time aches and pains? It may also signify that you have arthritis.

- Are you experiencing any pain in the gut or stomachache? The pain may create inflammation. Gut inflammation may also cause cramping, bloating, and loose stools.
- A swollen lymph node is another sign of inflammation. These nodes lie in the neck, armpits, and groin, which swell if there is a problem in your system. When you have a sore throat, your neck nodes lump because the body's defense system has sensed the condition. These lymph nodes react since the body is fighting the infection. The nodes reshape as you heal.
- Is your nose stuffed up? If indeed, maybe it is a symptom of irritating nasal tooth cavities.
- Sometimes, your epidermis may protrude because of internal inflammation.

Foods to Eat

If you already eat an appropriate healthy diet, you will have no trouble incorporating these foods into your meals. You may already be enjoying them and need a few tweaks to increase their presence in your meal planning. Some of the right foods that prevent and reduce chronic inflammation are as follows:

Omega-3 Fatty Acids

Omega-3 fatty acids are found in fish and fish oil. They calm the white blood cells and help them realize there is no danger to return to dormancy. Wild salmon and other fish are good sources; It is recommended to eat them three times a week. Other foods rich in Omega-3 are flax meal and dry beans such as navy beans, kidney beans, and soybeans. An Omega3 supplement may be helpful if you are not able to ingest enough of these foods.

Fruits and Vegetables

Most fruits and vegetables are anti-inflammatory. They are naturally rich in antioxidants, carotenoids, lycopene, and magnesium. Dark green leafy vegetables and colorful fruits and berries do much to inhibit white blood cell activity.

Protective Oils and Fats

Yes, there are a few oils and fats that are good for chronic inflammation sufferers. They include coconut oil and extra virgin olive oil. Butter or cream is also acceptable to consume. Ghee, made from butter, is even better because it has the lactose and casein removed – the very ingredients cause so much trouble if you have lactose intolerance or wheat sensitivity.

Fiber

Fiber keeps waste moving through the body. Since the vast majority of our immune cells reside in the intestines, it is essential to keep your gut happy. If that doesn't provide enough fiber, feel free to take a fiber supplement.

Miscellaneous

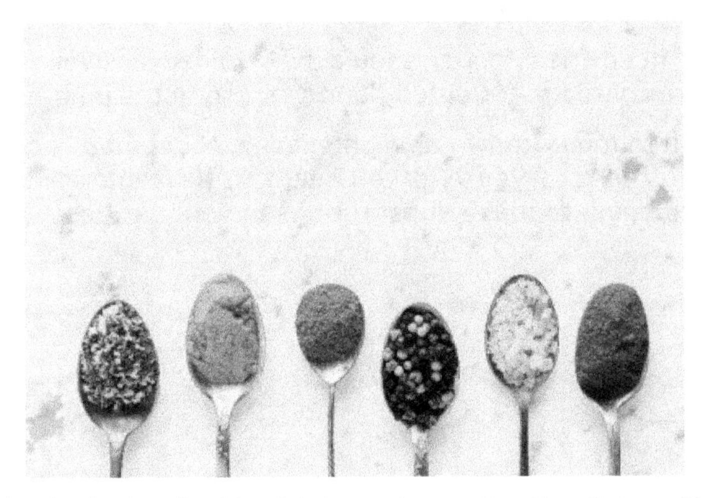

Eat foods with spices and herbs instead of bad fats and unsafe oils. Spices like turmeric, cumin, cloves, ginger, and cinnamon can enhance white blood cells' calming. Herbs like fennel, rosemary, sage, and thyme also reduce inflammation while adding delicious new flavors to your food.

Fermented foods like sauerkraut, buttermilk, yogurt, and kimchi contain helpful bacteria that prevent inflammation.

Healthy snacks would include a limited amount of unsweetened, plain yogurt with fruit mixed in, celery, carrots, pistachios, almonds, walnuts, and other fruits and vegetables.

Foods to Avoid

While many foods should be included in your diet to aid in reducing chronic inflammation, there are also some foods that you must avoid to help keep the inflammation down.

Processed foods and sugars are two of the biggest culprits when it comes to inflammation in the western diet. Processed foods are highly refined, causing them to lose much of their natural fiber and nutrients. They are often high in omega-6, trans fats, and saturated fats, increasing inflammation.

Sugar is one of the worst offenders when it comes to increased inflammation. Not only does it hide in many foods, studies have found that it is also very addictive. Because of this, you should expect to go through a withdrawal phase when you remove it from your diet. It can often cause headaches, cravings, and sluggishness. Give yourself some time to allow your body to work through it. You don't have to remove natural sugars from your diet entirely, but you should work towards eating them a few times a week and at no more than one meal per day.

Most fried foods, especially deep-fried foods, should be avoided as well. Usually, they are cooked in processed oils or lard and are coated in a refined flour that promotes inflammation.

You will want to pay attention to foods known as nightshades. Nightshades can be anti-inflammatory, but some people are sensitive to them; if you find you seem to have more inflammation after consuming nightshade, you may want to begin to make substitutions in your recipes.

CHAPTER 2:

Main Benefits of Anti-Inflammatory Diet

Studies argue that an anti-inflammatory diet may contribute to relieving symptoms of several health conditions.

Atherosclerosis can be described as a buildup of plaque in the arteries and is common among the elderly. The researchers observed a link between subclinical atherosclerosis and heart-disease-linked death; sticking to an anti-inflammatory diet can help lower specific inflammatory markers in individuals with type 2 diabetes. Individuals battling type 2 diabetes and adhering exclusively to the recommended Mediterranean diet report lower inflammation symptoms than those who do not practice any anti-inflammatory diet.

The Mediterranean diet has significant similarities as an anti-inflammatory diet. The Mediterranean diet involves selecting and preparing foods that have protein and push for switching to low-fat dairy products. Adherents of a Mediterranean diet prefer healthy plant-based protein such as beans, nuts, and seeds that can also provide the right amount of dietary fiber. As indicated, antioxidants are essential in our diets to help prevent or delay cell damage. It is encouraged that you select vegetables and fruits across the color spectrum to allow control and lessen inflammation and provide steady energy. An anti-inflammatory diet should also allow various minerals and vitamins, essential fatty acids, dietary fiber, and protective phytonutrients.

Furthermore, sticking to an anti-inflammatory diet can help avoid obesity. An anti-inflammatory diet argues against consuming excess calories that can translate to an accumulation of fatty tissue, causing obesity. Inflammatory diet and obesity may align in several ways. One, inflammation diet implies taking more refined carbohydrates, processed meats, and junk food. Due to these foods' low-calorie nature and the absence or low fiber, a person will have to compensate for the calorie shortage and feeling of fullness by eating more than necessary. Two, an individual consuming an inflammatory diet may spend more time seated and indoors, which inadvertently pushes the person to consume more and engage less in exercises.

Notably, an anti-inflammatory diet can help manage inflammatory-related conditions for those already affected. For instance, anti-inflammatory calls for cutting out refined sugars and starches can cause type 2 diabetes, metabolic syndrome, and obesity. Instead, anti-inflammatory diet advocates for the consumption of whole grains such as brown rice rich in fiber and has a low glycemic load.

In this manner, adhering to the anti-inflammatory diet increases an individual's health status in the long-term. An anti-inflammatory diet proposes reducing eating saturated and trans fatty acids and instead advocates for increased intake of omega-3 fatty acids. Consumption of unhealthy fats has been associated with an increased risk of cardiovascular diseases. One of the adverse effects of unhealthy fats is that they get deposited on the walls of blood vessels, making them narrower, which increases blood pressure. Increased blood pressure can damage the blood vessels and other organs that have to adjust to more than the usual flow rate of blood. The anti-inflammatory diet guideline pushes for the intake of heart-healthy oils such as olive oil or flaxseed.

Correspondingly, the anti-inflammatory diet can lower blood pressure. An anti-inflammatory diet can help you lose unwanted weight because it reduces refined carbohydrates and unhealthy fats. An anti-inflammatory diet also implies that eating nutrient-dense food helps the need for excessive eating, all of which contribute to unhealthy weight gain and obesity. The consumption of whole and unprocessed foods also helps create the fullness needed and avert excessive food consumption leading to weight gain. Gathering fat deposits in the blood vessels will lead to narrowing and, eventually, high blood pressure. Most processed foods also contain salt as a part of the preservatives, and high table salt intake increases blood pressure. With this in mind, an anti-inflammatory diet is critical in addressing blood pressure in the long-term.

Additionally, an anti-inflammatory diet can lower fatigue. Any form of inflammation implies that the immune system is engaged. When the immune system becomes fully committed, then histamine levels also increase, making a person feel exhausted, tired, and moody. It is thought that fatigue due to the immune system's actions means to slow down your body and conserve energy. Fatigue is also believed to help you rest and heal first than constraining the body further. An anti-inflammatory diet helps to minimize or eliminate inflammation, thus removing or lessening the immune system's effects that cause fatigue.

Not related to obesity, an anti-inflammatory diet can help one shed unwanted weight. Even if you are not obese, you could be overweight or bordering on being fat. High intake of refined carbohydrates and sugars are blamed for unplanned weight gain and other non-dietary causes such as sedentary lifestyles. Refined carbohydrate consumables tend to have low nutrients, implying that one consumes more than necessary to attain the calories needed. Additionally, refined carbohydrate consumables lack fiber, which means that one does not feel full and consumes excessively relative to their body size. Fortunately, an anti-inflammatory diet eliminates refined carbohydrates and encourages the consumption of other nutrition-dense consumables, implying that one cuts down on harmful sugars and carbohydrates.

There are also indirect benefits of adhering to an anti-inflammatory diet. One of these benefits is that an individual will become more settled due to minimizing inflammation occasioned by dietary practices. Some of the signs of inflammation include pain, fatigue, swelling, and immobility. Inflammation, in this perspective, can cause absence at the workplace or school. Inflammation can lead to discomfort during work or schools, making one have trouble with concentration. By addressing dietary triggers of inflammation, an individual will have more chances of attaining expected focus at work or school.

An anti-inflammatory diet can promote good sleep. Diet can contribute to a low quality of sleep or erratic sleep pattern in multiple ways. A diet that increases inflammation implies that you will have difficulties getting regular sleep, and when you get it, the sleep will be of low quality. An inflammatory diet can cause eating disorders such as waking up at night to eat, which disrupts the quality and duration of sleep you are having. Due to fatigue, you might need frequent bouts of short sleeping, which will affect night sleep. Fortunately, an anti-inflammatory diet can fix diet-related causes of poor sleep by ensuring that you experience less inflammation and ensure that your meals have adequate calories and nutrients.

Finally, an anti-inflammatory diet promotes choice and variety, allowing other dietary plans to blend from it. An anti-inflammatory diet captures a general approach to any diet that lessens or eliminates inflammation but still packs nutrients and calories requisite for daily intake. As a broad diet, several diets align with the anti-inflammatory diet, such as vegan diets and Mediterranean diets. By not being restrictive, an anti-inflammatory diet allows individuals to choose, which is a critical factor for any dietary approach's success. Openness in a dietary plan is necessary because of factors such as availability, cost, cultural significance, and seasonality that affect the choice of what consumes.

CHAPTER 3:

Meal Prep Plans Week 1 and 2

Day	Breakfast	Lunch	Dinner	Snacks/Sides
WEEK 1				
Monday	Turmeric Oven Scrambled Eggs	Capellini Soup with Tofu and Shrimp	Roasted Vegetables with Sweet Potatoes and White Beans	Steamed Broccoli
Tuesday	Breakfast Oatmeal	Iceberg Lettuce and Mushrooms Salad	Roasted Tofu and Greens	Boiled Cabbage
Wednesday	Blueberry Smoothie	Arugula with Gorgonzola Dressing	Tofu and Italian-Seasoned Summer Vegetables	Vegetable "Cheese" Sauce
Thursday	Breakfast Porridge	Fusilli with Grape Tomatoes and Kale	Spiced Broccoli, Cauliflower, and Tofu with Red Onion	Purple Cabbage Salad with Quinoa and Edamame
Friday	Quinoa and Asparagus Mushroom Frittata	Rice and Chicken Pot	Tempeh and Root Vegetable Bake	Steamed Cauliflower
Saturday	Cherry Spinach Smoothie	Shiitake and Spinach Pattie	Garlicky Chicken and Vegetables	Saucy Brussel Sprouts and Carrots
Sunday	Tropical Carrot Ginger and Turmeric Smoothie	Cabbage Orange Salad with Citrusy Vinaigrette	Turmeric-Spiced Sweet Potatoes, Apple, and Onion with Chicken	Lemony Cauliflower Rice
WEEK 2				
Monday	Golden Milk Chia Pudding	Lemon Buttery Shrimp Rice	Honey-roasted Chicken Thighs with Carrots	Lemony Steamed Asparagus
Tuesday	No-Bake Turmeric Protein Donuts	Valencia Salad	Sesame-tamari Baked Chicken with Green Beans	Lemon Garlic Red Chard
Wednesday	Choco-nana Pancakes	Tenderloin Stir Fry with Red and Green Grapes	Sheet Pan Turkey Breast with Golden Vegetables	Lemon Ginger Broccoli and Carrots
Thursday	Sweet Potato Cranberry Breakfast Bars	Aioli with Eggs	Sheet Pan Steak with Brussels Sprouts and Red Wine	Curried Mustard Greens
Friday	Savory Breakfast Pancakes	Aioli on Spaghetti Squash	Miso Salmon and Green Beans	"Cheesy" Brussel Sprouts and Carrots
Saturday	Scrambled Eggs with Smoked Salmon	Ginger Chicken Stew	Tilapia with Asparagus and Acorn Squash	Garlic Green Beans
Sunday	Raspberry Grapefruit Smoothie	Taro Leaves in Coconut Sauce	Shrimp-lime Bake with Zucchini and Corn	Simple Beet Salad

CHAPTER 4:

Meal Prep Plans Week 3 and 4

Day	Breakfast	Lunch	Dinner	Snacks/Sides
WEEK 3				
Monday	Breakfast Burgers with Avocado Buns	Seared Herbed Salmon Steak	Broccolini with Anchovy Almonds	Cabbage and Avocado Salsa
Tuesday	Spinach Mushroom Omelet	Smoked Salmon Salad	Tilapia with Pecan Rosemary Topping	Spinach Cabbage Slaw
Wednesday	Kale Turmeric Scramble	Turkey Couscous Pilaf	Steamed Trout with Red Bean and Chili Salsa	Chicken Pesto Salad
Thursday	Poached Salmon Egg Toast	Broccolini with Anchovy Almonds	Ratatouille	Peppers Avocado Salsa
Friday	Egg Muffins with Feta and Quinoa	Amaranth and Quinoa Stuffed Peppers	Italian Stuffed Peppers	Chard Spread
Saturday	Cream Cheese Salmon Toast	Barbeque Ocean Trout with Garlic and Parsley Dressing	Lemon Herb Salmon and Zucchini	Olives Coconut Dip
Sunday	Weekend Breakfast Salad	Smashed Chickpea Avocado Salad Sandwich with Cranberries	Sweet Potato Black Beans Burgers	Basil Peppers Dip
WEEK 4				
Monday	Carrot Cake Overnight Oats	Delicious Tuna Salad	Turkey and Quinoa Stuffed Peppers	Watercress Salsa
Tuesday	Kiwi Strawberry Smoothie	Turkey Chili	Avocado Pesto Zoodles with Salmon	Beef Bites
Wednesday	Mediterranean Frittata	Kale Caesar Salad with Grilled Chicken Wrap	Salmon Cakes	Cheese Stuffed Bell Peppers
Thursday	Maple Oatmeal	Baked Tilapia Recipe with Pecan Rosemary Topping	Chicken and Snap Pea Stir Fry	Olive Parsley Spread
Friday	Tomato Oatmeal	Clean Eating Egg Salad	Balsamic Chicken	Basic Mushroom Salsa
Saturday	Chia Breakfast Pudding	Winter Style Fruit Salad	Pineapple Fried Rice	Shrimp with Okra Bowls
Sunday	Slow Cooker French Toast Casserole	Easy Salmon Salad	Chicken Roast with Turmeric and Fennel	Thyme Celery Spread

CHAPTER 5:

Meal Prep Plans Week 5 and 6

Day	Breakfast	Lunch	Dinner	Snacks/Sides
WEEK 5				
Monday	Crackpot Banana Foster	Healthy Pasta Salad	Roasted Salmon with Potatoes and Romaine	Nutmeg Spiced Endives
Tuesday	Chicken and Quinoa Burrito Bowl	Spinach Bean Salad	Quinoa Salad	Cucumber-Yogurt Dip
Wednesday	Nutty Blueberry Banana Oatmeal	Kale Salad	Broccoli Tuna	White Bean Dip
Thursday	Slow Cooker Steamed Cinnamon Apples	Sweet Potato Soup	Cauliflower Rice	Mashed Avocado with Jicama Slices
Friday	Carrot Rice with Scrambled Eggs	Curry Lentil Stew	Orange Chicken Salad	Creamy Broccoli Dip
Saturday	Breakfast Tofu	Black Bean Tortilla Wrap	Vegetable Soup	Smoked Trout and Mango Wraps
Sunday	Breakfast Frittata	Sweet Potato Patties	Beets Gazpacho	Kale Chips
WEEK 6				
Monday	Breakfast Potatoes	Coconut Mushroom Soup	Lentil Curry	Smoked Turkey-Wrapped Zucchini Sticks
Tuesday	Breakfast Omelet	Tomato Detox Soup	Creamy Turmeric Cauliflower Soup	Crunchy Chickpeas
Wednesday	Breakfast Stuffed Biscuits	Cauliflower Soup	"Eat Your Greens" Soup	Sweet Potato Chips
Thursday	Breakfast Avocado Boat	Bean Shawarma Salad	Sweet Potato and Corn Soup	Mini Snack Muffins
Friday	Breakfast Casserole	Pesto Pasta with Walnut Sage & Delicious Squash	Chickpea Curry Soup	Chia-Strawberry Ice Pops
Saturday	Sweet Potato Hash	Feta Frittata & Spinach	Brown Rice and Shitake Miso Soup with Scallions	Broccoli-Sesame Stir-Fry
Sunday	Green Shakshuka	Coconut Green Curry with Boil Rice	Garlic and Lentil Soup	Dill and Salmon Pate

CHAPTER 6:

Meal Prep Plans Week 7 and 8

Day	Breakfast	Lunch	Dinner	Snacks/Sides
WEEK 7				
Monday	5-Minute Golden Milk	Chicken Salad with Chinese Touch	Italian Summer Squash Soup	Chickpea-Garlic Hummus
Tuesday	Steel Cut Oats with Kefir and Berries	Lentil Soup with Spices	Chicken and Gluten-free Noodle Soup	Turmeric Bars
Wednesday	Rhubarb, Apple plus Ginger Muffin Recipe	Baked Sweet Potato with Red Tahini Sauce	Leek, Chicken, and Spinach Soup	Turmeric Gummies
Thursday	Mushroom and Spinach Frittata	Bake Chicken Top-up with Olives, Tomatoes, and Basil	Saffron and Salmon Soup	Ginger Spiced Mixed Nuts
Friday	Gluten-Free Crepes	Sweet Potato & Chicken Soup with Lentil	Butternut Squash Soup with Shrimp	Spicy Tuna Rolls
Saturday	Amaranth Porridge with Roasted Pears	White Bean Chicken with Winter Green Vegetables	Clear Clam Chowder	Veggie Burrito
Sunday	Turkey Apple Breakfast Hash	Garlic Shrimps with Gritted Cauliflower	White Bean Chili	Spicy Kale Chips
WEEK 8				
Monday	No-Bake Chocolate Chia Energy Bars	Garlic & Squash Noodles	Layered Greek-Style Vegetables	Ginger Date Bars
Tuesday	Buckwheat Cinnamon and Ginger Granola	Garlic Chicken Bake with Basil & Tomatoes	Mushroom, Kale, and Sweet Potato Brown Rice	Vanilla Turmeric Orange Juice
Wednesday	Peaches with Honey Almond Ricotta	Smoked Trout Wrapped in Lettuce	Broccolini with Anchovy Almonds	Hibiscus Ginger Gelatin
Thursday	Quinoa Breakfast Bowl	Crusted Salmon with Walnuts & Rosemary	Tilapia with Pecan Rosemary Topping	Turmeric Nuggets
Friday	Fruity Flaxseed Breakfast Bowl	Healthy Pasta Salad	Steamed Trout with Red Bean and Chili Salsa	Coconut Flour Muffins
Saturday	Perky Paleo Potato & Protein Powder	Spinach Bean Salad	Ratatouille	No-Bake Golden Energy Bites
Sunday	Spicy Shakshuka	Kale Salad	Italian Stuffed Peppers	Banana Ginger Bars

CHAPTER 7:

Meal Prep Plans Week 9 and 10

Day	Breakfast	Lunch	Dinner	Snacks/Sides
WEEK 9				
Monday	Choco Chia Banana Bowl	Sweet Potato Soup	Italian Stuffed Peppers	Kombucha Gummies
Tuesday	Power Protein Porridge	Curry Lentil Stew	Lemon Herb Salmon and Zucchini	Cacao Coffee Protein Bars
Wednesday	Avo Toast with Egg	Black Bean Tortilla Wrap	Sweet Potato Black Beans Burgers	Steamed Broccoli
Thursday	Quick Quinoa with Cinnamon & Chia	Sweet Potato Patties	Turkey and Quinoa Stuffed Peppers	Boiled Cabbage
Friday	Plum, Pear & Berry-Baked Brown Rice Recipe	Coconut Mushroom Soup	Avocado Pesto Zoodles with Salmon	Vegetable "Cheese" Sauce
Saturday	Swift & Spicy Energy Eggs	Tomato Detox Soup	Salmon Cakes	Purple Cabbage Salad with Quinoa and Edamame
Sunday	Banana Bread Overnight Oats	Cauliflower Soup	Chicken and Snap Pea Stir Fry	Steamed Cauliflower
WEEK 10				
Monday	Good Grains with Cranberries & Cinnamon	Cauliflower Soup	Balsamic Chicken	Saucy Brussel Sprouts and Carrots
Tuesday	Fresh & Fruity Perky Parfait	Bean Shawarma Salad	Pineapple Fried Rice	Lemony Cauliflower Rice
Wednesday	Seared Syrupy Sage Pork Patties	Pesto Pasta with Walnut Sage & Delicious Squash	Chicken Roast with Turmeric and Fennel	Lemony Steamed Asparagus
Thursday	Creamy Cinnamon Banana Bowl	Feta Frittata & Spinach	Roasted Salmon with Potatoes and Romaine	Lemon Garlic Red Chard
Friday	Turkey with Thyme & Sage Sausage	Coconut Green Curry with Boil Rice	Quinoa Salad	Lemon Ginger Broccoli and Carrots
Saturday	Crackpot Banana Foster	Chicken Salad with Chinese Touch	Broccoli Tuna	Curried Mustard Greens
Sunday	Chicken and Quinoa Burrito Bowl	Lentil Soup with Spices	Cauliflower Rice	"Cheesy" Brussel Sprouts and Carrots

CHAPTER 8:

Staples

Pistachio Pesto

Preparation Time: 5 minutes

Cooking Time: 0 minutes

Servings: 4

Ingredients:

- 2 Cups Basil Leaves, Fresh & Packed Tight
- 1 cup Pistachios, Raw
- ½ Cup Olive Oil, Divided
- ½ Cup Parmesan Cheese, Shredded
- 2 Teaspoon Lemon Juice, Fresh
- ½ Teaspoon Garlic Powder
- Sea Salt & Black Pepper to Taste

Directions:

Get out your food processor, blend your basil, pistachios, and a quarter cup of olive oil together for fifteen seconds.

Throw in your cheese, lemon juice, garlic powder, and then season with salt and pepper.

Pour in your remaining olive oil, and make sure it's mixed well. Serve immediately, and it will keep in the fridge for five days.

Nutrition:

- Calories: 229
- Protein: 5.5 Grams
- Fat: 3.6 Grams
- Carbs: 3.8 Grams

Caesar Dressing

Preparation Time: 5 minutes

Cooking Time: 0 minutes

Servings: 2

Ingredients:

- ¼ Cup Paleo mayonnaise
- 2 Tablespoons Olive Oil
- 2 Cloves Garlic, Minced
- ½ Teaspoon Anchovy Paste
- 1 Tablespoon White Wine Vinegar
- ½ Teaspoon Lemon Zest
- 2 Tablespoons Lemon Juice, Fresh
- Sea Salt & Black Pepper to Taste

Directions:

Whisk all of your ingredients together. It should be emulsified and combined. Put salt and pepper, and then refrigerate it for up to a week.

Nutrition:

- Calories: 167
- Protein: 0.2 Grams
- Fat: 18.9 Grams
- Carbs: 1.3 Grams

Beans

Preparation Time: 5 minutes

Cooking Time: 1 hour

Servings: 5

Ingredients:

- 8 Ounces Beans, Dried
- Filtered Water (for Soaking & Cooking)
- 1 Bay leaf
- 1 Teaspoon Garlic
- 1 Teaspoon Onion Powder
- ½ Teaspoon Cumin
- Pinch Sea Salt, Fine

Directions:

Get out a glass bowl and add in your beans. Cover them with water, and then add a dash of salt. Soak for eight hours.

Drain them, and make sure to rinse well—transfer to a pot, and then season.

Put about two inches of water, and then cook on high heat. Boil, and then reduce it to low. Allow it to simmer for an hour. Serve.

Nutrition:

- Calories: 153

- Protein: 10 Grams
- Fat: 1 Gram
- Carbs: 28 Grams

Lemon Dijon Dressing

Preparation Time: 10 minutes

Cooking Time: 0 minutes

Servings: 13

Ingredients:

- ¼ Cup Olive Oil
- 1 Teaspoon Dijon Mustard
- ½ Teaspoon Honey, Raw
- ¼ Teaspoon Basil
- 1 Clove Garlic, Minced
- ¼ Teaspoon Sea Salt, Fine
- 2 Tablespoons Lemon Juice, Fresh

Directions:

Mix all ingredients, and shake vigorously. Refrigerate for up to a week.

Nutrition:

- Calories: 128
- Protein: 0.1 Gram
- Fat: 1.8 Grams
- Carbs: 1.8 Grams

Tahini & Lime Dressing

Preparation Time: 5 minutes

Cooking Time: 0 minutes

Servings: 1

Ingredients:

- 3 Tablespoons Water
- 2 Tablespoons Lime Juice Fresh
- 1 Tablespoon Apple Cider Vinegar
- 1/3 cup Tahini (Sesame Paste)
- 1 Teaspoon Lime Zest
- 1 ½ Teaspoons Honey, Raw
- Pinch Sea Salt, Fine
- ¼ Teaspoon Garlic Powder

Directions:

Combine everything, and shake until combined. Serve.

Nutrition:

- Calories: 157
- Protein: 6.2 Grams
- Fat: 2.1 Grams
- Carbs: 5.1 Grams

Everything Aioli

Preparation Time: 5 minutes

Cooking Time: 0 minutes

Servings: 2

Ingredients:

- ½ Cup Whole Milk
- 2 Teaspoons Dijon Mustard
- ¼ Teaspoon Honey, Raw
- ½ Teaspoon Hot Sauce
- Pinch Sea Salt

Directions:

Mix everything, and it will keep in the fridge for up to three days.

Nutrition:

- Calories: 43
- Protein: 2 Grams
- Fat: 2.4 Grams
- Carbs: 3.2 Grams

Almond Romesco Sauce

Preparation Time: 5 minutes

Cooking Time: 20 minutes

Servings: 2

Ingredients:

- 2 Red Bell Peppers, Chopped Rough
- 6 Cherry Tomatoes, Chopped Rough
- 3 Cloves Garlic, Chopped Rough
- ½ White Onion, Chopped Rough
- 1 Tablespoon Avocado Oil

- 1 cup Raw Almonds, Blanched
- ¼ Cup Olive Oil
- 2 Tablespoons Apple Cider Vinegar
- Sea Salt & Black Pepper to taste

Directions:

Turn your broiler to high and allow it to preheat. Get out a baking sheet and line it with foil.

Spread your tomatoes, onion, garlic, and bell pepper onto your baking sheet, and drizzle it with avocado oil. Broil this for ten minutes, and then get out a blender.

Pulse your almonds until they are crumbly.

Add in your olive oil, vinegar, vegetables, salt, and pepper. Process until smooth. It can keep in the fridge for up to five days. Alternatively, you can freeze it, and it will keep for three months.

Nutrition:

- Calories: 358
- Protein: 7.3 Grams
- Fat: 32.2 Grams
- Carbs: 13.7 Grams

Honey-Lime Vinaigrette with Fresh Herbs

Preparation Time: 10 minutes

Cooking Time: 0 minutes

Servings: 1

Ingredients:

- Juice of 4 limes
- 3 tablespoons honey
- 2 tablespoons apple cider vinegar
- 2 tablespoons Dijon mustard
- 2 garlic cloves, minced
- 3 scallions, finely chopped
- ½ cup roughly chopped fresh cilantro

Directions:

Whisk the lime juice, honey, vinegar, mustard, and garlic in a medium bowl. Put the scallions and cilantro, stir.

Storage: Store in a screw-top jar in the refrigerator for up to 5 days.

Substitution tip: For a spicier vinaigrette, add ½ teaspoon of chili powder or red pepper flakes.

Nutrition:

- Calories: 82
- Total Fat: 1g
- Protein: 1g
- Total Carbohydrates: 21g
- Fiber: 2g
- Sugar: 16g
- Cholesterol: 0mg

Simple Citrus Vinaigrette Dressing

Preparation Time: 10 minutes

Cooking Time: 0 minutes

Servings: 1

Ingredients:

- Juice of 1 lemon
- 2 tablespoons apple cider vinegar
- 2 tablespoons olive oil
- ½ teaspoon Dijon mustard
- 1 garlic clove, minced
- ¾ teaspoon salt
- 1 teaspoon freshly ground black pepper
- ½ teaspoon dried oregano
- ½ teaspoon dried thyme

Directions:

Mixer the lemon juice, vinegar, oil, mustard, garlic, salt, pepper, oregano, and thyme in a medium bowl. Serve.

Nutrition:

- Calories: 54
- Total Fat: 5g
- Saturated Fat: 1g
- Protein: 0g
- Total Carbohydrates: 1g
- Fiber: 0g
- Sugar: 0g
- Cholesterol: 0mg

Zesty Vegan Caesar Dressing

Preparation Time: 10 minutes

Cooking Time: 0 minutes

Servings: 1

Ingredients:

- ¼ cup tahini
- 1 teaspoon Dijon mustard
- Juice of 1 lemon
- 2 teaspoons capers, minced
- 3 garlic cloves, minced
- 1 teaspoon maple syrup
- ½ teaspoon salt
- ½ teaspoon freshly ground black pepper
- 1 or 2 tablespoons cold water

Directions:

Mix the tahini, mustard, lemon juice, capers, garlic, maple syrup, salt, and pepper in a medium bowl. Put the water 1 tablespoon at a time if needed to thin the dressing to a pourable consistency.

Nutrition:

- Calories: 82
- Total Fat: 7g
- Saturated Fat: 1g
- Protein: 2g
- Total Carbohydrates: 5g
- Fiber: 1g
- Sugar: 1g
- Cholesterol: 0mg

Creamy Avocado Dressing

Preparation Time: 10 minutes

Cooking Time: 0 minutes

Servings: 1

Ingredients:

- 1 avocado, halved and pitted
- 1 tablespoon olive oil
- 2 teaspoons apple cider vinegar
- 1 garlic clove, peeled but whole
- Juice of 1 lemon
- ½ teaspoon onion powder
- 1 teaspoon maple syrup
- 1 teaspoon Dijon mustard
- ½ teaspoon salt
- ½ teaspoon freshly ground black pepper
- 10 tablespoons cold water

Directions:

Process the avocado flesh into a food processor. Add the oil, vinegar, garlic, lemon juice, onion powder, maple syrup, mustard, salt, and pepper and pulse the mixture until it's smooth and creamy. Add as much water as you need, 1 tablespoon at a time, to thin it to a thick but pourable consistency.

Nutrition:

- Calories: 105
- Total Fat: 9g
- Saturated Fat: 2g
- Protein: 1g
- Total Carbohydrates: 7g
- Fiber: 4g
- Sugar: 3g
- Cholesterol: 0mg

Simple Ginger Teriyaki Sauce

Preparation Time: 5 minutes

Cooking Time: 5 minutes

Servings: 1

Ingredients:

- ¼ cup tamari
- 3 tablespoons cold water, plus 1½ teaspoons
- 2 tablespoons honey
- 2 tablespoons rice vinegar
- 1 garlic clove, minced
- ½ teaspoon sriracha
- 1½ teaspoons grated fresh ginger
- 1½ teaspoons arrowroot powder or cornstarch

Directions:

Mix the tamari, 3 tablespoons of water, the honey, vinegar, garlic, sriracha, and ginger in a medium bowl. Transfer to a medium saucepan and heat it over medium-high heat.

While the tamari mixture is heating, in a small bowl, combine the remaining 1½ teaspoons of water and the arrowroot powder, mixing well to incorporate. Thicken for at least 2 to 3 minutes.

Once the tamari mixture boils, reduce the heat to medium-low and whisk in the arrowroot mixture. Continue to whisk the sauce in the pan for 1 to 2 minutes more until it thickens slightly. Set it aside.

There will be some larger pieces of garlic and ginger in this sauce. For a smoother sauce, blend in a blender for 10 to 20 seconds, until the ginger and garlic are completely incorporated.

Nutrition:

- Calories: 40
- Total Fat: 0g
- Saturated Fat: 0g
- Protein: 2g
- Total Carbohydrates: 9g
- Fiber: 0g
- Sugar: 7g
- Cholesterol: 0mg

Avocado Crema

Preparation Time: 5 minutes

Cooking Time: 0 minutes

Servings: 1

Ingredients:

- 1 avocado, halved and pitted
- ¼ cup full-fat coconut milk
- Juice of 1 lime
- ¼ teaspoon salt
- ¼ cup fresh cilantro leaves

Directions:

Process the avocado flesh into a food processor. Add the coconut milk, lime juice, salt, and cilantro and pulse the mixture until it's smooth and creamy.

Nutrition:

- Calories: 122
- Total Fat: 11g
- Saturated Fat: 4g
- Protein: 2g
- Total Carbohydrates: 7g
- Fiber: 4g
- Sugar: 2g
- Cholesterol: 0mg

Basic Brown Rice

Preparation Time: 10 minutes

Cooking Time: 55 minutes

Servings: 2

Ingredients:

- 1 cup of brown rice
- 2½ cups water
- ½ teaspoon salt

Directions:

Mix the rice, water, plus salt in a medium saucepan. Simmer, uncovered, over medium-high heat.

Set the heat to low, cover, then simmer within 45 minutes. Do not stir the rice during cooking.

When no liquid remains, remove the pan from the heat and set it aside to cool for 10 minutes.

Fluff the rice gently using a fork to avoid sticking.

Nutrition:

- Calories: 138
- Total Fat: 1g
- Saturated Fat: 0g
- Protein: 3g
- Total Carbohydrates: 29g
- Fiber: 1g
- Sugar: 0g
- Cholesterol: 0mg

Savory Herbed Quinoa

Preparation Time: 10 minutes

Cooking Time: 20 minutes

Servings: 3

Ingredients:

- 1 cup quinoa, rinsed
- 2 cups vegetable broth
- 1½ tablespoons olive oil
- Juice of ½ lemon
- ½ teaspoon salt
- ½ teaspoon freshly ground black pepper
- ½ cup chopped fresh parsley
- ½ cup chopped fresh basil
- 2 scallions, chopped

Directions:

Mix the quinoa and broth in a saucepan and bring to a boil over high heat. Set the heat to medium-low, cover, then simmer for 15 to 20 minutes.

Remove from the heat and let rest, covered, for 10 minutes more.

Transfer to a large bowl and put the olive oil, lemon juice, salt, pepper, parsley, basil, and scallions. Stir to incorporate.

Nutrition:

- Calories: 175
- Total Fat: 6g
- Saturated Fat: 1g
- Protein: 5g
- Total Carbohydrates: 25g
- Fiber: 3g
- Sugar: 2g
- Cholesterol: 0mg

Garlic-Herb Marinated Tempeh or Tofu

Preparation Time: 30 minutes

Cooking Time: 20 minutes

Servings: 3

Ingredients:

- 8 ounces tempeh
- 2 tablespoons olive oil
- ¼ cup vegetable broth or water
- 1 tablespoon white wine vinegar
- 3 garlic cloves, minced
- 1½ teaspoons dried thyme
- ½ teaspoon salt
- ½ teaspoon freshly ground black pepper

Directions:

Preheat the oven to 400°F. Line a sheet pan with parchment paper.

Slice the tempeh in crosswise into 1-inch-thick slices. For the marinade, combine the oil, broth, vinegar, garlic, thyme, salt, and pepper in a large bowl. Place the tempeh in the marinade and use a spoon to coat it thoroughly. Marinate for at least 10 minutes, then flip or toss and marinate for 10 minutes more.

Pour the tempeh onto the sheet pan in a single layer. Pour any additional marinade onto the pan and bake for 15 to 20 minutes.

Nutrition:

- Calories: 233
- Total Fat: 17g
- Saturated Fat: 3g
- Protein: 14g
- Total Carbohydrates: 9g
- Fiber: 0g
- Sugar: 0g
- Cholesterol: 0mg

CHAPTER 9:

Breakfast

Turmeric Oven Scrambled Eggs

Preparation Time: 10 minutes

Cooking Time: 15 minutes

Servings: 6

Ingredients:

- 8 to 10 large eggs, pasture-raised
- ½ cup unsweetened almond or coconut milk
- ½ teaspoon turmeric powder
- 1 teaspoon chopped cilantro
- ¼ teaspoon black pepper
- A pinch of salt

Directions:

Preheat the oven to 3500F.

Grease a casserole or heat-proof baking dish.

In a bowl, whisk the egg, milk, turmeric powder, black pepper, and salt.

Pour in the egg mixture into the baking dish—Bake within 15 minutes.

Remove, then garnish with chopped cilantro on top.

Nutrition:

- Calories 203
- Total Fat 16g
- Total Carbs 5g
- Protein 10g
- Sugar: 4g
- Fiber: 1g
- Sodium: 303 mg

Breakfast Oatmeal

Preparation Time: 5 minutes

Cooking Time: 8 minutes

Servings: 1

Ingredients:

- 2/3 cup coconut milk
- 1 egg white, pasture-raised
- ½ cup gluten-free quick-cooking oats
- ½ teaspoon turmeric powder
- ½ teaspoon cinnamon
- ¼ teaspoon ginger

Directions:

Place the non-dairy milk in a saucepan and heat over medium flame.

Stir in the egg white and continue whisking until the mixture becomes smooth.

Put in the rest of the fixing and cook for another 3 minutes.

Nutrition:

- Calories 395
- Total Fat 34g
- Total Carbs 19g
- Protein 10g
- Sugar: 2g
- Fiber: 3g
- Sodium: 76mg

Blueberry Smoothie

Preparation Time: 5 minutes

Cooking Time: 0 minutes

Servings: 1

Ingredients:

- 1 cup almond milk
- 1 frozen banana
- 1 cup frozen blueberries
- 2 handful spinach
- 1 tablespoon almond butter
- ¼ teaspoon cinnamon
- ¼ teaspoon cayenne pepper
- 1 teaspoon maca powder

Directions:

Pulse all the fixing in a blender until well-combined. Serve immediately.

Nutrition:

- Calories 431
- Total Fat 21g
- Total Carbs 56g
- Net Carbs 48g
- Protein 10g
- Sugar: 38g
- Fiber: 8g
- Sodium: 201mg

Breakfast Porridge

Preparation Time: 15 minutes

Cooking Time: 0 minutes

Servings: 1

Ingredients:

- 6 tablespoons organic cottage cheese
- 3 tablespoons flaxseed
- 3 tablespoons flax oil
- 2 tablespoons organic raw almond butter
- 1 tablespoon organic coconut meat
- 1 tablespoon raw honey
- ¼ cup of water

Directions:

Combine all ingredients in a bowl. Mix until well combined.

Place in a bowl and chill before serving.

Nutrition:

- Calories 632
- Total Fat 49g
- Total Carbs 32g
- Net Carbs 26g
- Protein 23g
- Sugar: 22g
- Fiber: 6g
- Sodium: 265mg

Quinoa and Asparagus Mushroom Frittata

Preparation Time: 5 minutes

Cooking Time: 30 minutes

Servings: 3

Ingredients:

- 2 tablespoons olive oil
- 1 cup sliced mushrooms
- 1 cup asparagus, cut into 1-inch pieces
- ½ cup chopped tomato
- 6 large eggs, pasture-raised
- 2 large egg whites, pasture-raised
- ¼ cup non-dairy milk
- 1 cup quinoa, cooked according to package instructions
- 3 tablespoons chopped basil
- 1 tablespoon chopped parsley, garnish
- salt and pepper to taste

Directions:

Preheat the oven to 3500F.

Warm the olive oil over medium flame in a skillet.

Stir in the mushrooms and asparagus—season with salt and pepper to taste. Sauté for 7 minutes or until the mushrooms and asparagus have browned. Add the tomatoes and cook for another 3 minutes. Set aside.

Meanwhile, mix the eggs, egg white, and milk in a mixing bowl. Set aside.

Place in a baking dish the quinoa and top with the vegetable mixture. Pour in the egg mixture.

Bake within 20 minutes or until the eggs have set.

Nutrition:

- Calories 450
- Total Fat 37g
- Total Carbs 17g
- Net Carbs 14g
- Protein 12g
- Sugar: 2g
- Fiber: 3g
- Sodium: 60mg

Cherry Spinach Smoothie

Preparation Time: 5 minutes

Cooking Time: 0 minutes

Servings: 1

Ingredients:

- 1 cup plain kefir
- 1 cup frozen cherries, pitted
- ½ cup baby spinach leaves
- ¼ cup mashed ripe avocado
- 1 tablespoon almond butter
- 1-piece peeled ginger (1/2 inch)
- 1 teaspoon chia seeds

Directions:

Place all ingredients in a blender. Pulse until smooth.

Allow chilling in the fridge before serving.

Nutrition:

- Calories 410
- Total Fat 20g
- Total Carbs 47g
- Net Carbs 37g
- Protein 17g
- Sugar: 33g
- Fiber: 10g
- Sodium: 169mg

Tropical Carrot Ginger and Turmeric Smoothie

Preparation Time: 5 minutes

Cooking Time: 0 minutes

Servings: 1

Ingredients:

- 1 blood orange, peeled and seeded
- 1 large carrot, peeled and chopped
- ½ cup frozen mango chunks
- 2/3 cup coconut water
- 1 tablespoon raw hemp seeds
- ¾ teaspoon grated ginger
- 1 ½ teaspoon peeled and grated turmeric
- A pinch of cayenne pepper
- A pinch of salt

Directions:

Blend all fixings in a blender until smooth.

Chill before serving.

Nutrition:

- Calories 259
- Total Fat 6g
- Total Carbs 51g
- Net Carbs 40g
- Protein 7g
- Sugar: 34g
- Fiber: 11g
- Sodium: 225mg

Golden Milk Chia Pudding

Preparation Time: 6 hours

Cooking Time: 0 minutes

Servings: 4

Ingredients:

- 4 cups of coconut milk
- 3 tablespoons honey
- 1 teaspoon vanilla extract
- 1 teaspoon ground turmeric
- ½ teaspoon ground cinnamon
- ½ teaspoon ground ginger
- ¾ cup of coconut yogurt
- ½ cup chia seeds
- 1 cup fresh mixed berry
- ¼ cup toasted coconut chips

Directions:

Mix the coconut milk, honey, vanilla extract, turmeric, cinnamon, and ginger in a bowl. Add in the coconut yogurt.

In bowls, place chia seeds, berries, and coconut chips.

Pour in the milk mixture.

Allow chilling in the fridge to set for 6 hours.

Nutrition:

- Calories 337
- Total Fat 11g
- Total Carbs 51g
- Protein 10g
- Sugar: 29g
- Fiber: 2g
- Sodium: 262mg

No-Bake Turmeric Protein Donuts

Preparation Time: 50 minutes

Cooking Time: 0 minutes

Servings: 8

Ingredients:

- 1 ½ cups raw cashews
- ½ cup Medjool dates pitted
- 1 tablespoon vanilla protein powder
- ½ cup shredded coconut
- 2 tablespoons maple syrup
- ¼ teaspoon vanilla extract
- 1 teaspoon turmeric powder
- ¼ cup dark chocolate

Directions:

Mix all items except for the chocolate in a food processor.

Pulse until smooth.

Roll batter into 8 balls and press into a silicone donut mold.

Chill for 30 minutes to set.

Meanwhile, make the chocolate topping by melting the chocolate in a double boiler.

Once the donuts have set, remove the donuts from the mold and drizzle with chocolate.

Nutrition:

- Calories 320
- Total Fat 26g
- Total Carbs 20g
- Protein 7g
- Sugar: 9g
- Fiber: 2g
- Sodium:163 mg

Choco-Nana Pancakes

Preparation Time: 5 minutes

Cooking Time: 6 minutes

Servings: 2

Ingredients:

- 2 large bananas, peeled and mashed
- 2 large eggs, pasture-raised
- 3 tablespoon cacao powder
- 2 tablespoons almond butter
- 1 teaspoon pure vanilla extract
- 1/8 teaspoon salt
- Coconut oil for greasing

Directions:

Preheat a skillet on medium-low heat and grease the pan with coconut oil.

Place all ingredients in a food processor and pulse until smooth.

Pour a batter (about ¼ cup) onto the skillet and form a pancake.

Cook for 3 minutes on each side.

Nutrition:

- Calories 303
- Total Fat 17g
- Total Carbs 36g
- Protein 5g
- Sugar: 15g
- Fiber: 5g
- Sodium: 108mg

Sweet Potato Cranberry Breakfast bars

Preparation Time: 10 minutes

Cooking Time: 40 minutes

Servings: 8

Ingredients:

- 1 ½ cups sweet potato puree
- 2 tablespoons coconut oil, melted
- 2 tablespoons maple syrup
- 2 eggs, pasture-raised
- 1 cup almond meal
- 1/3 cup coconut flour
- 1 ½ teaspoon baking soda
- 1 cup fresh cranberry, pitted and chopped
- ¼ cup of water

Directions:

Preheat the oven to 3500F.

Grease a baking pan with coconut oil. Set aside.

Combine the sweet potato puree, water, coconut oil, maple syrup, and eggs in a mixing bowl.

In another bowl, sift the almond flour, coconut flour, and baking soda.

Put the dry fixing to the wet fixing. Mix.

Put into the baking pan and press the cranberries on top.

Bake for 40 minutes or until a toothpick inserted in the middle comes out clean.

Allow to rest or cool before removing from the pan.

Nutrition:

- Calories 98
- Total Fat 6g
- Total Carbs 9g
- Protein 3g
- Sugar: 7g
- Fiber: 0.5g
- Sodium:113 mg

Savory Breakfast Pancakes

Preparation Time: 5 minutes

Cooking Time: 6 minutes

Servings: 4

Ingredients:

- ½ cup almond flour
- ½ cup tapioca flour
- 1 cup of coconut milk
- ½ teaspoon chili powder
- ¼ teaspoon turmeric powder
- ½ red onion, chopped
- 1 handful cilantro leaves, chopped
- ½ inch ginger, grated
- 1 teaspoon salt
- ¼ teaspoon ground black pepper

Directions:

Mix all the fixing until well-combined in a bowl.

Heat a pan on low, medium heat and grease with oil.

Pour ¼ cup of batter onto the pan and spread the mixture to create a pancake.

Fry for 3 minutes per side.

Nutrition:

- Calories 108
- Total Fat 2g
- Total Carbs 20g
- Protein 2g
- Sugar: 4g
- Fiber: 0.5g
- Sodium: 37mg
- Potassium 95mg

Scrambled Eggs with Smoked Salmon

Preparation Time: 10 minutes

Cooking Time: 10 minutes

Servings: 2

Ingredients:

- 4 eggs
- 2 tablespoons coconut milk
- Fresh chives, chopped
- 4 slices of wild-caught smoked salmon, chopped
- salt to taste

Directions:

Whisk the egg, coconut milk, plus chives in a bowl.

Grease the skillet with oil and heat over medium-low heat.

Put the egg batter, then scramble it while cooking.

When the eggs start to settle, add in the smoked salmon and cook for 2 more minutes.

Nutrition:

- Calories 349
- Total Fat 23g
- Total Carbs 3g
- Protein 29g
- Sugar: 2g
- Fiber: 2g
- Sodium: 466mg

Raspberry Grapefruit Smoothie

Preparation Time: 5 minutes

Cooking Time: 0 minutes

Servings: 1

Ingredients:

- Juice from 1 grapefruit, freshly squeezed
- 1 banana, peeled and sliced
- 1 cup raspberries

Directions:

Pulse all fixing in a blender until smooth. Chill before serving.

Nutrition:

- Calories 381
- Total Fat 0.8g
- Total Carbs 96g
- Net Carbs 85g
- Protein 4g
- Sugar: 61g
- Fiber: 11g
- Sodium: 11mg
- Potassium 848mg

Breakfast Burgers with Avocado Buns

Preparation Time: 10 minutes

Cooking Time: 5 minutes

Servings: 1

Ingredients:

- 1 ripe avocado
- 1 egg, pasture-raised
- 1 red onion slice
- 1 tomato slice
- 1 lettuce leaf
- Sesame seed for garnish
- salt to taste

Directions:

Slice the avocado into half. It will serve as the bun. Set aside.

Grease a skillet over medium flame and fry the egg sunny-side up for 5 minutes or until set.

Assemble the breakfast burger by placing on top of one avocado half with the egg, red onion, tomato, and lettuce leaf. Top with the remaining avocado bun.

Garnish with sesame seeds on top and season with salt to taste.

Nutrition:

- Calories 458
- Total Fat 39g
- Total Carbs 20g
- Protein 13g
- Sugar: 8g
- Fiber: 14g

Spinach Mushroom Omelet

Preparation Time: 3 minutes

Cooking Time: 15 minutes

Servings: 2

Ingredients:

- Olive oil, one tablespoon + one tablespoon
- Spinach, fresh, chopped, one- and one-half cup

- Green onion, one diced
- Eggs, three
- Feta cheese, one ounce
- Mushrooms, button, five sliced
- Red onion, diced, one quarter cup

Directions:

Sauté the mushrooms, onions, and spinach for three minutes in one tablespoon of olive oil and set to the side. Beat the eggs well and cook them in the other tablespoon of olive oil for three to four minutes until edges begin to brown. Sprinkle all the other ingredients onto half of the omelet and fold the other half over the sautéed ingredients. Cook for one minute on each side.

Nutrition:

- Calories 337
- fat 25 grams
- protein 22 grams
- carbs 5.4 grams
- sugar 1.3 grams
- fiber 1-gram

Weekend Breakfast Salad

Preparation Time: 30 minutes

Cooking Time: 0 minutes

Servings: 4

Ingredients:

- Eggs, four hard-boiled
- Lemon, one
- Arugula, ten cups
- Quinoa, one cup cooked and cooled
- Olive oil, two tablespoons
- Dill, chopped, one half cup
- Almonds, chopped, one cup
- Avocado, one large sliced thin
- Cucumber, chopped, one half cup
- Tomato, one large cut in wedges

Directions:

Mix the quinoa, cucumber, tomatoes, and arugula. Toss these ingredients lightly together with olive oil, salt, and pepper. Transfer and arrange the egg and avocado on top. Top each salad with almonds and herbs. Drizzle with juice from the lemon.

Nutrition:

- Calories 336
- fat 7.7 grams
- protein 12.3 grams
- carbs 54.6 grams
- sugar 5.5 grams
- fiber 5.2 grams

Kale Turmeric Scramble

Preparation Time: 5 minutes

Cooking Time: 10 minutes

Servings: 1

Ingredients:

- Olive oil, two tablespoons
- Kale, shredded, one half cup
- Sprouts, one half cup
- Garlic, minced, one tablespoon
- Black pepper, one quarter teaspoon
- Turmeric, ground, one tablespoon
- Eggs, two

Directions:

Beat the eggs and add in the turmeric, black pepper, and garlic. Sauté the kale into the olive oil over medium heat for five minutes, and then pour this egg batter into the pan with the kale. Continue cooking, often stirring, until the eggs are cooked. Top with raw sprouts and serve.

Nutrition:

- Calories 137
- fat 8.4 grams
- carbs 7.9 grams
- fiber 4.8 grams
- sugar 1.8grams
- protein 13.2 grams

Poached Salmon Egg Toast

Preparation Time: 10 minutes

Cooking Time: 4 minutes

Servings: 2

Ingredients:

- Bread, two slices rye or whole-grain toasted
- Lemon juice, one quarter teaspoon
- Avocado, two tablespoons mashed
- Black pepper, one quarter teaspoon
- Eggs, two poached
- Salmon, smoked, four ounces
- Scallions, one tablespoon sliced thin
- Salt, one eighth teaspoon

Directions:

Add lemon juice to avocado with pepper and salt. Spread the mixed avocado over the toasted bread slices. Lay smoked salmon over toast and top with a poached egg. Top with sliced scallions.

Nutrition:

- Calories 389
- fat 17.2 grams
- protein 33.5 grams
- carbs 31.5 grams
- sugar 1.3 grams
- fiber 9.3 grams

Egg Muffins with Feta and Quinoa

Preparation Time: 15 minutes

Cooking Time: 30 minutes

Servings: 12

Ingredients:

- Eggs, eight
- Tomatoes, chopped, one cup
- Salt, one quarter teaspoon
- Feta cheese, one cup
- Quinoa, one cup cooked
- Olive oil, two teaspoons
- Oregano, fresh chop, one tablespoon
- Black olives, chopped, one quarter cup
- Onion, chopped, one quarter cup
- Baby spinach, chopped, two cups

Directions:

Heat oven to 350. Spray oil a muffin pan with twelve cups. Cook spinach, oregano, olives, onion, and tomatoes for five minutes in the olive oil over medium heat. Beat eggs. Add the cooked mix of veggies to the eggs with the cheese and salt. Spoon mixture into muffin cups. Bake thirty minutes. These will remain fresh in the fridge for two days. To eat, just wrap in a paper towel and warm in the microwave for thirty seconds.

Nutrition:

- Calorie 113
- carbs 5 grams
- protein 6 grams
- fat 7 grams
- sugar 1-gram

Peaches with Honey Almond Ricotta

Preparation Time: 15 minutes

Cooking Time: 0 minutes

Servings: 6

Ingredients:

- Spread
- Ricotta, skim milk, one cup
- Honey, one teaspoon
- Almonds, thin slices, one half cup
- Almond extract, one quarter teaspoon

To Serve

- Peaches, sliced, one cup
- Bread, whole grain bagel or toast

Directions:

Mix the almond extract, honey, ricotta, and almonds. Spread one tablespoon of this mix on toasted bread and cover with peaches.

Nutrition:

- Calories 230
- protein 9 grams

- fat 8 grams
- carbs grams 37
- fiber 3 grams
- sugar 34 grams

Quinoa Breakfast Bowl

Preparation Time: 30 minutes

Cooking Time: 0 minutes

Servings: 6

Ingredients:

- Quinoa, two cups cooked
- Eggs, twelve
- Greek yogurt, plain, one quarter cup
- Salt, one half teaspoon
- Feta cheese, one cup
- Cherry tomatoes, one pint cut in halves
- Black pepper, one teaspoon
- Garlic, minced, one teaspoon
- Baby spinach, chopped, one cup
- Olive oil, one teaspoon

Directions:

Mix the eggs, salt, pepper, garlic, onion powder, and yogurt. Cook the spinach and tomatoes for five minutes in the olive oil over medium heat. Pour in the egg mix and stir until eggs have set to your preferred doneness. Mix in quinoa and feta until they are hot. It will store in the fridge for two to three days.

Nutrition:

- Calories 340
- fat 7.3 grams
- carbs 59.4 grams
- fiber 6.2 grams
- sugar 21.4 grams
- protein 10.5 grams

Cream Cheese Salmon Toast

Preparation Time: 10 minutes

Cooking Time: 2 minutes

Servings: 2

Ingredients:

- Whole grain or rye toast, two slices
- Red onion, chopped fine, two tablespoons
- Cream cheese, low fat, two tablespoons
- Basil flakes, one half teaspoon
- Arugula or spinach, chopped, one half cup
- Smoked salmon, two ounces

Directions:

Toast the wheat bread. Mix cream cheese and basil and spread this mixture on the toast. Add salmon, arugula, and onion.

Nutrition:

- Calories 291
- fat 15.2 grams
- carbohydrates 17.8 grams
- sugar 3 grams

Carrot Cake Overnight Oats

Preparation Time: overnight

Cooking Time: 1 minute

Servings: 2

Ingredients:

- Coconut or almond milk, one cup
- Chia seeds, one tablespoon
- Cinnamon, ground, one teaspoon
- Raisins, one half cup
- Cream cheese, low fat, two tablespoons at room temperature
- Carrot, one large peel, and shred
- Honey, two tablespoons
- Vanilla, one teaspoon

Directions:

Mix all of the listed items and store them in a safe refrigerator container overnight. Eat cold in the morning. If you choose to warm this, just microwave for one minute and stir well before eating.

Nutrition:

- Calories 340

- sugar 32 grams
- protein 8 grams
- fat 4 grams
- fiber 9 grams
- carbs 70 grams

Kiwi Strawberry Smoothie

Preparation Time: 10 minutes

Cooking Time: 0 minutes

Servings: 1

Ingredients:

- Kiwi, peeled and chopped, one
- Strawberries, fresh or frozen, one-half cup chopped
- Milk, almond or coconut, one cup
- Basil, ground, one teaspoon
- Turmeric, one teaspoon
- Banana, diced, one
- Chia seed powder, one quarter cup

Directions:

Drink immediately after all the ingredients have been well mixed.

Nutrition:

- Calories 250
- sugar 9.9 grams
- fat 1-gram
- grams 34 carbs
- fiber 4.3 grams

Mediterranean Frittata

Preparation Time: 5 minutes

Cooking Time: 20 minutes

Servings: 6

Ingredients:

- Eggs, six
- Feta cheese, crumbled, one quarter cup
- Black pepper, one quarter teaspoon
- Oil, spray, or olive
- Oregano, one teaspoon
- Milk, almond or coconut, one quarter cup
- Sea salt, one teaspoon
- Black olives, chopped, one quarter cup
- Green olives, chopped, one quarter cup
- Tomatoes, diced, one quarter cup

Directions:

Heat oven to 400. Oil one eight by eight-inch baking dish. Combine the milk into the eggs, and then add other ingredients. Pour all of this mixture into the baking dish and bake for twenty minutes.

Nutrition:

- Calories 107
- sugars 2 grams
- fat 7 grams
- carb 3 grams
- protein 7 grams

Maple Oatmeal

Preparation Time: 5 minutes

Cooking Time: 20 minutes

Servings: 4

Ingredients:

- Maple flavoring, one teaspoon
- Cinnamon, one teaspoon
- Sunflower seeds, three tablespoons
- Pecans, one-half cup chopped
- Coconut flakes, unsweetened, one quarter cup
- Walnuts, one-half cup chopped
- Milk, almond or coconut, one half cup
- Chia seeds, four tablespoons

Directions:

Pulse the sunflower seeds, walnuts, and pecans in a food processor to crumble. Or you can just put the nuts in a sturdy plastic bag, wrap the bag with a towel, lay it on a sturdy surface, and beat the towel with a hammer until the nuts are crumbled. Mix the crushed nuts with the rest of the ingredients and pour them into a large pot. Simmer this mixture over low heat for thirty minutes. Stir often, so the mix does not stick to the bottom. Serve garnished with fresh fruit or a sprinkle of cinnamon if desired.

Nutrition:

- Calories 374
- carbs 3.2 grams
- protein 9.25 grams
- fat 34.59 grams

Tomato Omelet

Preparation Time: 20 minutes

Cooking Time: 8 minutes

Servings: 1

Ingredients:

- Eggs, two
- Basil, fresh, one half cup
- Cherry tomatoes, one half cup
- Black pepper, one teaspoon
- Cheese, any type, one-quarter cup shredded
- Salt, one half teaspoon
- Olive oil, two tablespoons

Directions:

Cut the tomatoes into quarters. Fry it in the olive oil for three minutes. Set the tomatoes off to the side. Put salt and pepper to the eggs in a small bowl and beat together well. Pour the beaten egg mixture into the pan and use a spatula to gently work around the edges under the omelet, letting the eggs fry unmoved for three minutes. When the center third of the egg mix is still runny, add on the basil, tomatoes, and cheese. Fold over half of the omelet onto the other half. Cook two more minutes and serve.

Nutrition:

- Calories 342
- carbs 8 grams
- protein 20 grams
- fat 25.3 grams

Chia Breakfast Pudding

Preparation Time: 3 minutes

Cooking Time: 0 minutes

Servings: 2

Ingredients:

- Chia seeds, four tablespoons
- Almond butter, one tablespoon
- Coconut milk, three-fourths cup
- Cinnamon, one teaspoon
- Vanilla, one teaspoon
- Cold coffee, three-fourths cup

Directions:

Combine all of the fixings well and pour them into a refrigerator-safe container. Cover well and let refrigerate overnight.

Nutrition:

- Calories 282
- carbs 5 grams
- protein 5.9 grams
- fat 24 grams

Slow Cooker French toast Casserole

Preparation Time: 15 minutes

Cooking Time: 4 hours

Servings: 9

Ingredients:

- 2 eggs
- 2 egg whites
- 1 ½ almond milk or 1% milk
- 2 tbsp raw honey
- 1/2 tsp cinnamon
- 1 tsp vanilla extract
- 9 slices bread

For filling:

- 3cups apples (diced)
- 2 tbsp raw honey
- 1 tbsp lemon juice
- 1/2 tsp cinnamon
- 1/3 cup of pecans

Directions:

Put the first six items into a bowl and mix.

Grease the slow cooker with a non-stick cooking spray.

Combine all the ingredients of the filling in a small bowl and set aside. Coat the apple pieces into the filling properly.

Cut slices of bread in half (triangle), then place three apple slices on the bottom and some filing over. Layer the bread slices and filling in the same pattern.

Put the egg batter on the layers of bread and filling.

Set the cooker on high heat for 2 ½ hours or low heat for 4 hours.

Nutrition:

- Calories: 227
- Total Fat: 7g
- Carbohydrates: 34g
- Protein: 9g
- Sugar: 19g
- Fiber 4g
- Sodium: 187 mg

Crackpot Banana Foster

Preparation Time: 15 minutes

Cooking Time: 2 hours

Servings: 3

Ingredients:

- 1 tbsp melted coconut oil (unrefined)
- 3 tbsp honey
- 1/4 tsp cinnamon
- Juice of ½ medium-sized lemon
- 5 bananas (medium-sized)

For Garnish:

- Chopped nuts
- Greek Yogurt

Directions:

Put the first four items in the slow cooker and mix.

Cut the bananas in half and toss into the mixture inside the slow cooker.

Set on the cooker on low heat for 1 ½ to 2 hours.

Serve with chopped nuts or plain Greek yogurt.

Nutrition:

- Calories: 220
- Total Fat: 4g
- Carbohydrates: 56 g
- Protein: 4g
- Sugar: 36g
- Fiber 4g
- Sodium: 4 mg
- Cholesterol: 0mg

Chicken and Quinoa Burrito Bowl

Preparation Time: 10 minutes

Cooking Time: 5 hours

Servings: 6

Ingredients:

- 1 lb. chicken thighs (skinless, boneless)
- 1 cup of chicken broth
- 1 can have diced tomatoes (14.5oz)
- 1 onion (chopped)
- 3 cloves garlic (chopped)
- 2 tsp chili powder
- ½ tsp coriander
- ½ tsp garlic powder
- 1 bell pepper (finely chopped)
- 15oz pinto beans (drained)
- 1 ½ cup cheddar cheese (grated)

Directions:

Combine chicken, tomatoes, broth, onion, garlic, chili powder, garlic powder, coriander, and salt. Set the cooker on low heat.

Remove the chicken, and shred into pieces with a fork and knife.

Put the chicken back in the slow cooker and add quinoa and pinto beans.

Set the cooker on low heat for 2 hours.

Add cheese on to the top and continue to cook and stir gently until the cheese melts.

Serve.

Nutrition:

- Calories: 144mg
- Total Fat: 39g
- Carbohydrates: 68 g
- Protein: 59g
- Sugar: 8g
- Fiber 17g
- Sodium: 756 mg
- Cholesterol: 144mg

Nutty Blueberry Banana Oatmeal

Preparation Time: 10 minutes

Cooking Time: 2 hours

Servings: 6

Ingredients:

- 2 cup rolled eats
- 1/4 cup almonds (toasted)
- 1/4 cup walnuts
- 1/4 cup pecans
- 2 tbsp ground flax seeds
- 1 tsp ground ginger
- 1 tsp cinnamon
- 1/4 tsp sea salt
- 2 tbsp coconut sugar
- ½ tsp baking powder
- 2 cups of milk
- 2 bananas
- 1 cup fresh blueberries
- 1 tbsp maple syrup
- 1 tsp vanilla extract
- 1 tbsp melted butter
- Yogurt for serving

Directions:

In a large bowl, add nuts, flax seeds, baking powder, spices, and coconut sugar and mix.

In another bowl, beat eggs, milk, maple syrup, and vanilla extract.

Slice the bananas in half and layer them in the slow cooker pot with blueberries.

Add oats mixture and pour the milk mixture on the top.

Drizzle with melted butter,

Cook the slow cooker on low heat for 4 hours or on high heat for 4 hours. Cook till the liquid is absorbed and oats are golden brown.

Serve warm and top it off with plain Greek yogurt

Nutrition:

- Calories: 346 mg
- Total Fat: 15g
- Carbohydrates: 45g
- Protein: 11g
- Sugar: 17g
- Fiber 7g
- Sodium: 145 mg
- Cholesterol: 39mg

Slow Cooker Steamed Cinnamon Apples

Preparation Time: 15 minutes

Cooking Time: 4 hours

Servings: 6

Ingredients:

- 8 apples (peeled, cored)
- 2 tsp lemon juice
- 2 tsp cinnamon
- ½ tsp nutmeg
- ¼ cup of coconut sugar

Directions:

Put all the items in the slow cooker pot.

Set the slow cooker pot on a low setting for 3 to 4 hours.

Cook till the apples are tender. Serve.

Nutrition:

- Calories: 136
- Total Fat: 0g
- Carbohydrates: 36g

- Protein: 1g
- Sugar: 26g
- Fiber 5g
- Sodium: 6mg
- Cholesterol: 0mg

Carrot Rice with Scrambled Eggs

Preparation Time: 15 minutes

Cooking Time: 3 hours

Servings: 3

Ingredients:

For Sweet Tamari Soy Sauce

- 3 tbsp tamari sauce (gluten-free)
- 1 tbsp water
- 2-3 tbsp molasses

For Spicy Mix-ins

- 3 garlic cloves
- 1 small shallot (sliced)
- 2 long red chilies
- Pinch of ground ginger

For the Carrot Rice:

- 2 Tbsp sesame oil
- 5 eggs
- 4 large carrots
- 8 ounces sausage (chicken or any type of - gluten-free and minced).
- 1 tbsp sweet soy sauce
- 1 cup bean sprouts
- 1/2 cup fined diced broccoli
- salt and pepper to taste

For Garnish:

- Cilantro
- Asian chili sauce
- Sesame seeds

Directions:

For the Sauce:

In a saucepan, boil molasses, water, and tamari at a high flame.

Lower the flame after the sauce boils and cook till molasses is completely dissolved.

Place the sauce in a separate bowl.

For the Carrot Rice:

In a bowl, combine ginger, garlic, onion, and red chilies.

To make rice out of the carrots, spiralize the carrots in a spiralizer.

Pulse the spiralized carrots in a food processor.

Cut broccoli into small dice like pieces

Add the sausage, carrots, broccoli, and the bean sprouts into the bowl of onion, ginger, garlic, and chilies.

Add the spicy mix of vegetables and the tamari sauce in the slow cooker pot.

Set the cooker on high heat for 3 hours or low heat for 6 hours.

Scramble two eggs in a non-stick frying pan or skillet.

Dish out the carrot rice and add scrambled eggs on top.

Garnish with sesame seeds, Asian chili sauce, and cilantro.

Nutrition:

- Calories: 230 mg
- Total Fat: 13.7g
- Carbohydrates: 15.9g
- Protein: 12.2g
- Sugar: 8g
- Fiber 4.4g
- Sodium: 1060 mg
- Cholesterol: 239mg.

Breakfast Tofu

Preparation Time: 40 minutes

Cooking Time: 20 minutes

Servings: 4

Ingredients:

- 2 teaspoons toasted sesame oil
- 1 teaspoon rice vinegar
- 2 tablespoons reduced-sodium soy sauce

- ½ teaspoon onion powder
- 1 teaspoon garlic powder
- 1 block tofu, sliced into cubes
- 1 tablespoon potato starch

Directions:

In a bowl, combine all ingredients except tofu and potato starch.

Mix well.

Add tofu to the bowl.

Marinate for 30 minutes.

Coat tofu with the potato starch.

Add tofu to the air fryer basket.

Air fry at 370 degrees F for 20 minutes, shaking halfway through.

Nutrition:

- Calories: 177
- Carbs: 17g
- Fat: 7g
- Protein: 13g

Breakfast Frittata

Preparation Time: 15 minutes

Cooking Time: 20 minutes

Servings: 2

Ingredients:

- 1 onion, chopped
- 2 tablespoons red bell pepper, chopped
- ¼ lb. breakfast turkey sausage, cooked and crumbled
- 3 eggs, beaten
- Pinch cayenne pepper

Directions:

Mix all the ingredients in a bowl.

Pour into a small baking pan.

Add baking pan to the air fryer basket.

Cook in the air fryer for 20 minutes.

Nutrition:

- Calories: 207
- Carbs: 12g
- Fat: 11g
- Protein: 12g

Breakfast Potatoes

Preparation Time: 5 minutes

Cooking Time: 15 minutes

Servings: 2

Ingredients:

- 5 potatoes, sliced into cubes
- 1 tablespoon oil
- ½ teaspoon garlic powder
- ¼ teaspoon pepper
- ½ teaspoon smoked paprika

Directions:

Warm your air fryer at 400 degrees F for 5 minutes.

Toss potatoes in oil.

Season with garlic powder, pepper, and paprika.

Add potatoes to the air fryer basket.

Cook for 15 minutes.

Nutrition:

- Calories: 121
- Carbs: 19g
- Fat: 4g
- Protein: 2g

Breakfast Omelet

Preparation Time: 5 minutes

Cooking Time: 10 minutes

Servings: 2

Ingredients:

- 2 eggs, beaten
- 1 stalk green onion, chopped
- ½ cup mushrooms, sliced
- 1 red bell pepper, diced
- 1 teaspoon herb seasoning

Directions:

Beat eggs in a bowl. Stir in the rest of the ingredients.

Pour egg mixture into a small baking pan. Add pan to the air fryer basket.

Cook in the air fryer basket at 350 degrees F for 10 minutes.

Nutrition:

- Calories: 210
- Carbs: 5g
- Fat: 14g
- Protein: 15g

Breakfast Stuffed Biscuits

Preparation Time: 35 minutes

Cooking Time: 30 minutes

Servings: 10

Ingredients:

- 1 tablespoon vegetable oil
- ¼ lb. turkey sausage
- 2 eggs, beaten
- Pepper to taste
- 10 oz. refrigerated biscuits
- Cooking spray

Directions:

Heat-up the oil in a medium pan and cook sausage for 5 minutes.

Transfer to a bowl and set aside. Fry eggs in the pan, then season with pepper.

Add eggs to the bowl with sausage. Arrange biscuit dough in the air fryer.

Top each with the egg and sausage mixture. Fold up and seal.

Spray with oil. Cook in the air fryer at 325 degrees F for 8 minutes.

Flip and cook for another 7 minutes. Serve.

Nutrition:

- Calories: 98
- Carbs: 0g
- Fat: 0g
- Protein: 0g

Breakfast Avocado Boat

Preparation Time: 40 minutes

Cooking Time: 7 minutes

Servings: 2

Ingredients:

- 2 avocados, sliced in half and pitted
- ¼ onion, chopped
- 2 tomatoes, chopped
- 1 bell pepper, chopped
- 2 tablespoons cilantro, chopped
- Pepper to taste
- 4 eggs

Directions:

Chop the avocado flesh. Place in a bowl.

Stir in the rest of the fixing except the eggs.

Refrigerate for 30 minutes.

Crack the egg on top of the avocado shell.

Warm your air fryer to 350 degrees F. Air fry for 7 minutes.

Top with avocado salsa.

Nutrition:

- Calories: 458
- Carbs: 14g
- Fat: 38g
- Protein: 20g

Breakfast Casserole

Preparation Time: 10 minutes

Cooking Time: 10 minutes

Servings: 4

Ingredients:

- 1 lb. hash browns
- 1 lb. lean breakfast sausage, crumbled
- 1 yellow onion, chopped
- 1 red bell pepper, chopped
- 1 yellow bell pepper, chopped
- 1 green bell pepper, chopped
- Pepper to taste

Directions:

Arrange hash browns in the air fryer basket.

Top with sausage and veggies.

Air fry at 355 degrees F for 10 minutes.

Season with pepper.

Nutrition:

- Calories: 329
- Carbs: 9g
- Fat: 8g
- Protein: 21g

Sweet Potato Hash

Preparation Time: 10 minutes

Cooking Time: 15 minutes

Servings: 6

Ingredients:

- 2 sweet potatoes, sliced into cubes
- 2 tablespoons olive oil
- 1 tablespoon paprika
- 1 teaspoon dried dill weed
- Pepper to taste

Directions:

Warm your air fryer to 400 degrees F.

Combine all ingredients in a bowl.

Transfer to your air fryer.

Cook within 15 minutes, mixing every 5 minutes.

Nutrition:

- Calories: 176
- Carbs: 13g
- Fat: 6g
- Protein: 15g

Green Shakshuka

Preparation Time: 20 minutes

Cooking Time: 25 minutes

Servings: 4

Ingredients:

- 2 tablespoons extra-virgin olive oil
- 1 onion, minced
- 2 garlic cloves, minced
- 1 jalapeño, seeded and minced
- 1-pound spinach (thawed if frozen)
- 1 teaspoon dried cumin
- ¾ teaspoon coriander
- Salt and freshly ground black pepper
- 2 tablespoons harissa
- ½ cup vegetable broth
- 8 large eggs
- Chopped fresh parsley, as needed for serving
- Chopped fresh cilantro, as needed for serving
- Red-pepper flakes, as needed for serving

Directions:

Preheat the oven to 350 ° F.

Heat the olive oil inside a large, oven-safe skillet, over medium heat. Add the onion and sauté for 4 to 5 minutes. Stir in the garlic and jalapeño, then sauté 1 minute more until fragrant.

Add the spinach and cook until fully wilted if fresh, 4 to 5 minutes or 1 to 2 minutes if thawed from frozen, until heated through.

Season with cumin, pepper, coriander, salt, and harissa. Cook for approximately 1 minute, until fragrant.

Switch the mixture to a food processor bowl or a blender and puree until it is coarse. Connect the broth and purée until smooth and thick.

Wipe the skillet out and dust it with nonstick cooking spray. Pour the spinach mixture into the pan back and make eight circular wells using a wooden spoon.

Crack the eggs in the pipes, softly. Switch the skillet to the oven and cook for 20 to 25 minutes until the egg whites are set fully, but the yolks are still a little jiggly.

Sprinkle with parsley, cilantro, and red pepper flakes on the shakshuka, to taste. Serve straight away.

Nutrition:

- 251 calories
- 17g fat
- 10g carbs

- 17g protein
- 3g sugars

5-Minute Golden Milk

Preparation Time: 5 minutes

Cooking Time: 4 minutes

Servings: 1

Ingredients:

- 1 1/2 cups light coconut milk
- 1 1/2 cups unsweetened almond milk
- 1 1/2 tsp ground turmeric
- 1/4 tsp ground ginger
- 1 whole cinnamon stick
- 1 Tbsp coconut oil
- 1 pinch ground black pepper
- Sweetener of choice (i.e., coconut sugar, maple syrup, or stevia to taste)

Directions:

Add coconut milk, ground turmeric, almond milk, ground ginger, cinnamon stick, coconut oil, black pepper, and preferred sweetener to a small casserole.

Whisk to mix over medium heat and warm up. Heat to the touch until hot but do not boil-about 4 minutes-whisking regularly.

Turn off heat and taste to make flavor change. For strong spice + flavor, add more sweetener to taste, or more turmeric or ginger.

Serve straight away, break between two glasses, and leave the cinnamon stick behind. Best when fresh, although the leftovers can be kept 2-3 days in the refrigerator. Reheat up to temperature on the stovetop or microwave.

Nutrition:

- Calories: 205
- Fat: 19.5g
- Sodium: 161mg
- Carbohydrates: 8.9g
- Fiber: 1.1g
- Protein: 3.2g

Steel Cut Oats with Kefir and Berries

Preparation Time: 15 minutes

Cooking Time: 30 minutes

Servings: 4

Ingredients:

For the oats:

- 1 cup steel-cut oats
- 3 cups of water
- pinch of salt

For topping Optional:

- fresh or frozen fruit/berries
- a handful of sliced almonds, hemp seeds, pepitas, or other nuts/seeds
- unsweetened kefir, homemade/store-bought
- a drizzle of maple syrup, sprinkling of coconut sugar, a few drops of stevia, or any other sweetener you like, to taste

Directions:

Add/place the oats in a small saucepan and over medium-high heat. Make the pan toast, often stir or shake, for 2-3 minutes.

Adding the water and bring to a boil. Reduce heat to a cooker and let it cook for about 25 minutes, or until the oats are soft enough to satisfy you. Serve with berries, nuts/seeds, a splash of kefir, and any sweetener you like, to taste. Dig in!

Nutrition:

- Calories: 150
- Carbs: 27g
- Fat: 3g
- Protein: 4g

Rhubarb, Apple Plus Ginger Muffin Recipe

Preparation Time: 15 minutes

Cooking Time: 30 minutes

Servings: 8

Ingredients:

- 1/2 teaspoon ground cinnamon
- 1/2 teaspoon ground ginger

- pinch sea salt
- 1/2 cup almond meal (ground almonds)
- 1/4 cup unrefined raw sugar
- 2 tbsp finely chopped crystallized ginger
- 1 tbs ground linseed meal
- 1/2 cup buckwheat flour
- 1/4 cup fine brown rice flour
- 1/4 cup (60ml) olive oil
- 1 large free-range egg
- 1 teaspoon vanilla extract
- 2 tablespoons organic corn flour or true arrowroot
- 2 teaspoons gluten-free baking powder
- 1 cup finely sliced rhubarb
- 1 small apple, peeled and finely diced
- 95ml (1/3 cup + 1 tbsp) rice or almond milk

Directions:

Pre-heat the oven to 180C/350C. Grease or line 8 1/3 cup (80ml) cup muffin tins with a paper case cap.

In a medium bowl, put the almond meal, ginger, sugar, and linseed. Sieve over baking powder, flours, and spices and then mix evenly. In the flour mixture, whisk in rhubarb and apple to coat.

Whisk the milk, sugar, egg, and vanilla in another smaller bowl before pouring into the dry mixture and stirring until combined.

Divide the batter evenly between tins/paper cases and bake for 20 minutes -25 minutes or until it rises, golden around the edges.

Remove, then set aside for 5 minutes before transferring onto a wire rack to cool off further.

Eat warm or at room temperature.

Nutrition:

- Calories: 38
- Carbs: 9g
- Fat: 0g
- Protein: 0g

Mushroom and Spinach Frittata

Preparation Time: 15 minutes

Cooking Time: 30 minutes

Servings: 4

Ingredients:

- 6 eggs
- 1/4 cup (60 ml) milk
- 3 tablespoons (45 ml) butter
- 2 cups (500 ml) baby spinach
- Salt and pepper
- 1 cup grated cheddar cheese
- 1 onion, thinly sliced
- 4 oz white button mushrooms, sliced

Directions:

Pre-heat the oven up to 180 °C (350 °F), with the rack in the middle position. Butter a baking dish of 20 cm (8") square. Set aside.

Mix the eggs plus milk in a large bowl with a whisk. Stir in cheese. Season with pepper and salt. Set aside bowl.

Cook the onion, then mushrooms in butter over medium heat, in a large non-stick skillet. Season with pepper and salt. Put the spinach, then cook for about 1 minute, continually stirring.

Pour the mushroom mixture into a blend of eggs. Remove and pour over into a baking dish. Bake the frittata for about 25 mins, or until browned and puffed slightly. Cut the frittata into four squares and remove with a spatula from the platter. Place them on a plate, and voilà, they are ready to serve warm or cold.

Nutrition:

- Calories: 123
- Carbs: 4g
- Fat: 5g
- Protein: 15g

Gluten-Free Crepes

Preparation Time: 15 minutes

Cooking Time: 30 minutes

Servings: 10

Ingredients:

Option 1

- Making crepes using gluten-free and gum-free waffle and pancake mix
- 3 tablespoons sugar
- 1 1/2 cups gluten-free pancake mix
- 1 cup of cold water
- 2 eggs
- 2 tablespoons butter, melted

Option 2

- Making crepes using your favorite gluten-free and gum-free flour blend:
- 2 tablespoons butter, melted
- 3 tablespoons sugar
- 1 cup of cold water
- 2 tablespoons cold water
- 2 eggs
- 1 1/2 cups gluten-free flour
- 1/2 tsp gluten-free baking powder or mix baking soda and cream of tartar in equal parts
- 1/2 tsp vanilla extract

Directions:

In a large bowl, mix all crepe ingredients, and whisk the mixture until the lumps dissolve. Allow/let the mixture sit at room temperature for some 15 minutes. After 15 minutes, it will become thickened.

Heat the frying pan to very hot, spray it with oil spray and pour a small amount of batter into the frying pan using a soup spoon or 1/4 measuring cup as you roll the pan from side-side.

Allow this thin layer of crepe batter to cook for 1, 2, or 3 minutes, then turn the crepe to the other side, then let it cook for another minute.

Nutrition:

- Calories: 100
- Carbs: 14g
- Fat: 4g
- Protein: 3g

Amaranth Porridge with Roasted Pears

Preparation Time: 10 minutes

Cooking Time: 30 minutes

Servings: 2

Ingredients:

- ¼ teaspoon salt
- 2 tablespoons pecan pieces
- 1 teaspoon pure maple syrup
- 1 cup 0% Greek yogurt, for serving
- Pears
- Porridge
- ½ cup uncooked amaranth
- 1/2 cup water
- 1 cup 2% milk
- 1 teaspoon maple syrup
- 1 large pear
- 1/2 tsp ground cinnamon
- 1/4 tsp ground ginger
- 1/8 tsp ground nutmeg
- 1/8 tsp ground clove
- Pecan/Pear Topping

Directions:

Preheat the oven to 400 ° C.

Drain the amaranth, and rinse it. Combine with water, one cup of milk, and salt put the amaranth to a boil, and reduce it to a simmer. Cover and let it cook for 25 minutes until the amaranth is soft, but some liquid remains. Remove from heat, and allow the amaranth to thicken for another 5 to 10 minutes. If desired, apply a little more milk to smooth out the texture.

Toss the pecan parts together with the 1 tablespoon maple syrup. Roast for 10 mins to 15 minutes, until the pecans are toasted and the maple syrup has dried. When done, pecans can become relatively fragrant. When they cool down, pecans are crisp.

Dice the pears along with the pecans, and mix with the remaining 1 teaspoon of maple syrup and spices. Roast for 15 minutes in a roasting pan, until the pears are tender.

In the porridge, add 3/4 of the roasted pears. Divide yogurt into two bowls and cover with porridge, pecans roasted, and pear's remaining bits.

Nutrition:

- Calories: 55

- Carbs: 11g
- Fat: 2g
- Protein: 0g

Turkey Apple Breakfast Hash

Preparation Time: 15 minutes

Cooking Time: 10 minutes

Servings: 5

Ingredients:

For the meat:

- 1 lb. ground turkey
- 1 tablespoon coconut oil
- ½ teaspoon dried thyme
- ½ teaspoon cinnamon
- sea salt, to taste

For the hash:

- 1 tbsp coconut oil
- 1 onion
- 1 large apple, peeled, cored, and chopped
- 2 cups spinach or greens of choice
- ½ tsp turmeric
- ½ tsp dried thyme
- sea salt, to taste
- 1 large or 2 small zucchinis
- ½ cup shredded carrots
- 2 cups cubed frozen butternut squash (or the sweet potato)
- 1 tsp cinnamon
- ¾ tsp powdered ginger
- ½ tsp garlic powder

Directions:

In a skillet, heat a spoonful of coconut oil over medium/high heat. Attach turkey to the ground and cook until crispy. Season with thyme, cinnamon, and a pinch of sea salt. Move to the plate.

Throw remaining coconut oil into the same skillet and sauté onion until softened for 2-3 minutes.

Add the courgettes, apple, carrots, and frozen squash to taste—Cook for around 4-5 minutes, or until veggies soften.

Attach and whisk in spinach until wilted.

Add cooked turkey, seasoning, salt, and shut off oil.

Enjoy this hash fresh from the pan, or let it cool and refrigerate all week long. The hash can remain in a sealed container in the refrigerator for about 5-6 days.

Nutrition:

- Calories: 350
- Carbs: 20g
- Fat: 19g
- Protein: 28g

No-Bake Chocolate Chia Energy Bars

Preparation Time: 15 minutes

Cooking Time: 0 minutes

Servings: 14

Ingredients:

- 1 ½ cups packed, pitted dates
- 1/cup unsweetened shredded coconut
- 1 cup raw walnut pieces
- 1/4 cup (35 g) natural cocoa powder
- 1/2 cup (75 g) whole chia seeds
- 1/2 cup (70 g) chopped dark chocolate
- 1/2 cup (50 g) oats
- 1 tsp pure vanilla extract, optional, enhances the flavor
- 1/4 tsp unrefined sea salt

Directions:

Puree the dates in a blender until thick paste forms.

Add the walnuts and blend to mix.

Put the rest of the fixing and combine until a thick dough is formed.

Line a rectangular parchment-papered baking pan. Place the mixture tightly in the pan and place straight into all corners.

Place in the freezer until midnight, for at least a few hours.

Raise from the pan and cut into 14 strips.

Place in the refrigerator or an airtight container.

Nutrition:

- Sugar: 17 g
- Fat: 12 g
- Calories: 234
- Carbohydrates: 28 g
- Protein: 4.5 g

Buckwheat Cinnamon and Ginger Granola

Preparation Time: 15 minutes

Cooking Time: 40 minutes

Servings: 5

Ingredients:

- ¼ cup Chia seeds
- ½ Cup Coconut Flakes
- 1 ½ Cup mixed Raw nuts
- 2 cups of gluten-free oats
- 1 cup of buckwheat groats
- 2 tbsp nut butter
- 4 tbsp of coconut oil
- 1 cup of sunflower seeds
- ½ cup of pumpkin seeds
- 1 ½ - 2 inches piece of ginger
- 1 tsp Ground Cinnamon
- 1/3 cup of Rice Malt Syrup
- 4 tbsp of raw cacao powder – Optional

Directions:

Preheat the oven up to 180C

Blitz the nuts in your food processor and quickly blitz to chop roughly. Put the chopped nuts in a bowl and add all the other dry ingredients that combine well–oats, coconut, cinnamon, buckwheat, seeds, and salt in a low heat saucepan, melt the coconut oil gently.

Add the cacao powder (if used) to the wet mixture and blend. Put the wet batter over the dry mix, then mix well to make sure that everything is coated. Move the mixture to a wide baking tray lined with grease-proof paper or coconut oil greased. Be sure to uniformly distribute the mixture for 35-40 minutes, turning the mixture halfway through. Bake until the granola is fresh and golden!

Serve with your favorite nut milk, coconut yogurt scoop, fresh fruit, and superfoods–goji berries, flax seeds, bee pollen, whatever you like! Mix it up every single day.

Nutrition:

- Calories: 220
- Carbs: 38g
- Fat: 5g
- Protein: 7g

Fruity Flaxseed Breakfast Bowl

Preparation Time: 8 minutes

Cooking Time: 5 minutes

Servings: 1

Ingredients:

For the Porridge:

- ¼-cup flaxseeds, freshly ground
- ¼-tsp cinnamon, ground
- 1-cup almond or coconut milk
- 1 medium banana, mashed
- A pinch of fine-grained sea salt

For the Toppings:

- Blueberries, fresh or defrosted
- Walnuts, chopped raw
- Pure maple syrup (optional)

Directions:

In a medium-sized saucepan placed over medium heat, combine all the porridge ingredients. Stir constantly for 5 minutes, or until the porridge thickens and comes to a low boil.

Transfer the cooked porridge in a serving bowl. Garnish with the toppings and pour a bit of maple syrup if you want it a little sweeter.

Nutrition:

- Calories: 780

- Fat: 26g
- Protein: 39g
- Sodium: 270mg
- Total Carbs: 117.5g

Perky Paleo Potato & Protein Powder

Preparation Time: 8 minutes

Cooking Time: 0 minutes

Servings: 1

Ingredients:

- 1 small sweet potato, pre-baked and fleshed out
- 1-Tbsp protein powder
- 1 small banana, sliced
- ¼-cup blueberries
- ¼-cup raspberries
- Choice of toppings: cacao nibs, chia seeds, hemp hearts, favorite nut/seed butter (optional)

Directions:

In a small serving bowl, mash the sweet potato using a fork. Add the protein powder. Mix well until thoroughly combined.

Arrange the banana slices, blueberries, and raspberries on top of the mixture. Garnish with your desired toppings. You can relish this breakfast meal, either cold or warm.

Nutrition:

- Calories: 302
- Fat: 10g
- Protein: 15.3g
- Sodium: 65mg
- Total Carbs: 46.7g

Spicy Shakshuka

Preparation Time: 12 minutes

Cooking Time: 37 minutes

Servings: 4

Ingredients:

- 2-Tbsps extra-virgin olive oil
- 1-bulb onion, minced
- 1 jalapeño, seeded and minced
- 2-cloves garlic, minced
- 1-lb spinach
- Salt and freshly ground black pepper
- ¾-tsp coriander
- 1-tsp dried cumin
- 2-Tbsps harissa paste
- ½-cup vegetable broth
- 8-pcs large eggs
- Red pepper flakes, for serving
- Cilantro, chopped for serving
- Parsley, chopped for serving

Directions:

Preheat your oven to 350°F.

Heat the oil in an oven-safe skillet placed over medium heat. Stir in the onion and sauté for 5 minutes.

Add the jalapeño and garlic, and sauté for a minute, or until fragrant. Add in the spinach, and cook for 5 minutes, or until the leaves entirely wilt.

Season the mixture with salt and pepper, coriander, cumin, and harissa. Cook further for 1 minute.

Transfer the mixture to your food processor—puree to a thick consistency. Pour in the broth and puree further until achieving a smooth texture.

Clean and grease the same skillet with nonstick cooking spray. Pour the pureed mixture. By using a wooden spoon, form eight circular wells.

Crack each egg gently into the wells. Put the skillet in the oven—Bake for 25 minutes, or poaching the eggs until fully set.

To serve, sprinkle the shakshuka with red pepper flakes, cilantro, and parsley to taste.

Nutrition:

- Calories: 251
- Fat: 8.3g
- Protein: 12.5g
- Sodium: 165mg
- Total Carbs: 33.6g

Choco Chia Banana Bowl

Preparation Time: 4 hours & 5 minutes

Cooking Time: 0 minutes

Servings: 3

Ingredients:

- ½-cup chia seeds
- 1 large banana, very ripe
- ½-tsp pure vanilla extract
- 2-cups almond milk, unsweetened
- 1-Tbsp cacao powder
- 2-Tbsps raw honey or maple syrup
- 2-Tbsps cacao nibs for mixing in
- 2-Tbsps chocolate chips for mixing in
- 1 large banana, sliced for mixing in

Directions:

Combine the chia seeds and banana in a mixing bowl. By using a fork, mash the banana and mix well until thoroughly combined. Pour in the vanilla and almond milk. Whisk until no more lumps appear.

Pour half of the mix in a glass container, and cover it. Add the cacao and syrup to the remaining half mixture in the bowl. Mix well until fully incorporated. Pour this mixture in another glass container, and cover it. Chill for at least 4 hours.

To serve, layer the chilled chia puddings equally in three serving bowls. Alternate the layers with the ingredients for mixing-in.

Nutrition:

- Calories: 293
- Fat: 9.7g
- Protein: 14.6g
- Sodium: 35mg
- Total Carbs: 43.1g

Power Protein Porridge

Preparation Time: 15 minutes

Cooking Time: 8 minutes

Servings: 2

Ingredients:

- ¼-cup walnut or pecan halves, roughly chopped
- ¼-cup toasted coconut, unsweetened
- 2-Tbsps hemp seeds
- 2-Tbsps whole chia seeds
- ¾-cup almond milk, unsweetened
- ¼-cup coconut milk
- ¼-cup almond butter, roasted
- ½-tsp turmeric, ground
- 1-Tbsp extra virgin coconut oil or MCT oil
- 2-Tbsps erythritol or 5-10 drops liquid stevia (optional)
- A pinch of ground black pepper
- ½-tsp cinnamon or ½-tsp vanilla powder

Directions:

Put the walnuts, flaked coconut, and hemp seeds in a hot saucepan. Roast the mixture for 2 minutes, or until fragrant. Stir a few times to prevent burning. Transfer the roasted mix in a bowl. Set aside.

Combine the almond and coco milk in a small saucepan placed over medium heat. Heat the mixture.

After heating, but not boiling, switch off the heat. Add all the remaining ingredients. Mix well until thoroughly combined. Set aside for 10 minutes.

Combine half of the roasted mix with the porridge. Scoop the porridge into two serving bowls. Sprinkle each bowl with the remaining half of the roasted mixture and cinnamon powder. Serve the porridge immediately.

Nutrition:

- Calories: 572
- Fat: 19g
- Protein: 28.6g
- Sodium: 87mg
- Total Carbs: 81.5g
- Dietary Fiber: 10g

Avo Toast with Egg

Preparation Time: 15 minutes

Cooking Time: 0 minutes

Servings: 3

Ingredients:

- 1½-tsp ghee
- 1-slice bread, gluten-free and toasted
- ½ avocado, thinly sliced
- A handful of spinach
- 1 egg scrambled or poached
- A sprinkle of red pepper flakes

Directions:

Spread the ghee over the toasted bread. Top with the avocado slices and spinach leaves. Place a scrambled or poached egg on top. Finish off the garnishing with a sprinkle of red pepper flakes.

Nutrition:

- Calories: 540
- Fat: 18g
- Protein: 27g
- Sodium: 25mg
- Total Carbs: 73.5g
- Dietary Fiber: 6g

Quick Quinoa with Cinnamon & Chia

Preparation Time: 15 minutes

Cooking Time: 3 minutes

Servings: 2

Ingredients:

- 2-cups quinoa, pre-cooked
- 1-cup cashew milk
- ½-tsp ground cinnamon
- 1-cup fresh blueberries
- ¼-cup walnuts, toasted
- 2-tsp raw honey
- 1-Tbsp chia seeds

Directions:

Over medium-low heat, add the quinoa and cashew milk in a saucepan. Stir in the cinnamon, blueberries, and walnuts. Cook slowly for three minutes.

Remove the pan from the heat. Stir in the honey. Garnish with chia seeds on top before serving.

Nutrition:

- Calories: 887
- Fat: 29.5g
- Protein: 44.
- Sodium: 85mg
- Total Carbs: 129.3g
- Dietary Fiber: 18.5g

Plum, Pear & Berry-Baked Brown Rice Recipe

Preparation Time: 12 minutes

Cooking Time: 30 minutes

Servings: 2

Ingredients:

- 1-cup water
- ½-cup brown rice
- A pinch of cinnamon
- ½-tsp pure vanilla extract
- 2-Tbsps pure maple syrup (divided)
- Sliced fruits: berries, pears, or plums
- A bit of salt (optional)

Directions:

Preheat your oven to 400°F.

Bring the water and brown rice mixture to a boil in a pot placed over medium-high heat. Stir in the cinnamon and vanilla extract. Reduce the heat to medium-low. Simmer for 18 minutes, or until the brown rice is tender.

Fill two oven-safe bowls with equal portions of the rice. Pour a tablespoon of maple syrup in each bowl. Top the bowls with the sliced fruits and sprinkle over a pinch of salt if you desire.

Put the bowls in the oven—Bake for 12 minutes, or until the fruits start caramelizing, and the syrup begins bubbling.

Nutrition:

- Calories: 227
- Fat: 6.3g
- Protein: 14.1g

- Sodium: 80mg
- Total Carbs: 32.2g
- Dietary Fiber: 3.6g

Swift & Spicy Energy Eggs

Preparation Time: 2 minutes

Cooking Time: 3 minutes

Servings: 1

Ingredients:

- 1-Tbsp milk
- 1-tsp melted butter
- 2-pcs eggs
- A sprinkle of herbs and spices: dried dill, dried oregano, dried parsley, dried thyme, and garlic powder

Directions:

Preheat your oven to 325°F. Meanwhile, coat the bottom of a baking tray with the milk and butter.

Crack the eggs gently over milk and butter coating. Sprinkle the eggs with the dried herbs and garlic powder.

Put the tray in the oven. Bake for 3 minutes, or until the eggs cook through.

Nutrition:

- Calories: 177
- Fat: 5.9g
- Protein: 8.8g
- Sodium: 157mg
- Total Carbs: 22.8g
- Dietary Fiber: 0.7g

Banana Bread Overnight Oats

Preparation Time: 6 hours & 20 minutes

Cooking Time: 0 minutes

Servings: 3

Ingredients:

- ¼-cup plain Greek yogurt
- ¼-tsp flaked sea salt
- 1½-cups nonfat milk
- 1-cup old-fashioned rolled oats
- 1-Tbsp chia seeds
- 2-pcs medium bananas, very ripe and mashed
- 2-Tbsps coconut flakes, unsweetened and toasted
- 2-Tbsps honey
- 2-tsp vanilla extract
- Toppings for serving: roasted pecans, pomegranate seeds, honey, fig halves, and banana slices

Directions:

Stir in all of the ingredients, excluding the toppings, in a mixing bowl. Mix well until thoroughly combined. Divide the mixture equally between two serving bowls.

Cover and refrigerate overnight or for 6 hours.

To serve, stir, and put on the toppings.

Nutrition:

- Calories: 684
- Fat: 22.8g
- Protein: 34.2g
- Sodium: 374mg
- Total Carbs: 99.6g
- Dietary Fiber: 14.1g

Good Grains with Cranberries & Cinnamon

Preparation Time: 8 minutes

Cooking Time: 35 minutes

Servings: 2

Ingredients:

- 1-cup of grains (choice of amaranth, buckwheat, or quinoa)
- 2½-cups coconut water or almond milk
- 1-stick cinnamon
- 2-pcs whole cloves
- 1 star anise pod (optional)
- Fresh fruit: apples, blackberries, cranberries, pears, or persimmons
- Maple syrup (optional)

Directions:

Bring the grains, coconut water, and the spices to a boil in a saucepan. Cover, then lower the heat to medium-low. Simmer within 25 minutes.

To serve, discard the spices and top with fruit slices. If desired, drizzle with the maple syrup.

Nutrition:

- Calories: 628
- Fat: 20.9g
- Protein: 31.4g
- Sodium: 96mg
- Total Carbs: 112.3g
- Dietary Fiber: 33.8g

Fresh & Fruity Perky Parfait

Preparation Time: 20 minutes

Cooking Time: 0 minutes

Servings: 2

Ingredients:

- ½-cup fresh raspberries
- A pinch of cinnamon
- 1-tsp maple syrup
- 2-Tbsps chia seeds
- 16-oz. plain yogurt
- Fresh fruit: sliced blackberries, nectarines, or strawberries

Directions:

By using a fork, mash the raspberries in a mixing bowl until achieving a jam-like consistency. Add the cinnamon, syrup, and chia seeds. Continue mashing until incorporating all the ingredients. Set aside.

In two serving glasses, alternate layers of yogurt and the mixture. Garnish with fresh fruit slices.

Nutrition:

- Calories: 315
- Fat: 8.7g
- Protein: 19.6g
- Sodium: 164mg
- Total Carbs: 45.8g
- Dietary Fiber: 6.5g

Seared Syrupy Sage Pork Patties

Preparation Time: 12 minutes

Cooking Time: 10 minutes

Servings: 4

Ingredients:

- 2-lbs ground pork, pastured
- 3-Tbsps maple syrup, grade B
- 3-Tbsps minced fresh sage
- ¾-tsp sea salt
- ½-tsp garlic powder
- 1-tsp solid cooking fat

Directions:

Break the ground pork into chunks in a large mixing bowl. Drizzle evenly with the maple syrup. Sprinkle with the spices. Mix well until thoroughly combined. Form the mixture into eight patties. Set aside.

Heat the fat in a cast-iron skillet placed over medium heat. Cook the patties for 10 minutes on each side or until browned.

Nutrition:

- Calories: 405
- Fat: 11.2g
- Protein: 30.3g
- Sodium: 240mg
- Total Carbs: 53.3g
- Dietary Fiber: 0.8g
- Net Carbs: 45.5g

Creamy Cinnamon Banana Bowl

Preparation Time: 5 minutes

Cooking Time: 3 minutes

Servings: 1

Ingredients:

- 1 large banana, ripe
- ¼-tsp cinnamon, ground
- A pinch of Celtic sea salt
- 2-Tbsps coconut butter, melted

- Toppings of your choice: fruit, seed, or nut

Directions:

Mash the banana in a mixing bowl. Add the cinnamon and Celtic sea salt. Set aside.

Heat the coconut butter in a saucepan placed over low heat. Scoop the warm butter to the banana mixture.

To serve, top with your favorite fruit, seed, or nut.

Nutrition:

- Calories: 564
- Fat: 18.8g
- Protein: 28.2g
- Sodium: 230mg
- Total Carbs: 58.2g
- Dietary Fiber: 15.9g

Turkey with Thyme & Sage Sausage

Preparation Time: 40 minutes

Cooking Time: 25 minutes

Servings: 4

Ingredients:

- 1-lb ground turkey
- ½-tsp cinnamon
- ½-tsp garlic powder
- 1-tsp fresh rosemary
- 1-tsp fresh thyme
- 1-tsp sea salt
- 2-tsp fresh sage
- 2-Tbsps coconut oil

Directions:

Stir in all the ingredients, except for the oil, in a mixing bowl. Refrigerate overnight or for 30 minutes.

Pour the oil in the mixture. Form the mixture into four patties.

In a lightly greased skillet placed over medium heat, cook the patties for 5 minutes on each side, or until their middle portions are no longer pink. You can also cook them by baking in the oven for 25 minutes at 400°F.

Nutrition:

- Calories: 284
- Fat: 9.4g
- Protein: 14.2g
- Sodium: 290mg
- Total Carbs: 36.9g
- Dietary Fiber: 0.7g

CHAPTER 10:

Lunch Recipes

Capellini Soup with Tofu and Shrimp

Preparation Time: 20 mins

Cooking Time: 20 mins

Servings: 8

Ingredients:

- 4 cups of bok choy, sliced
- 1/4-pound shrimp, peeled, deveined
- 1 block firm tofu, sliced into squares
- 1 can sliced water chestnuts, drained
- 1 bunch scallions, sliced
- 2 cups reduced-sodium chicken broth
- 2 teaspoons soy sauce, reduced-sodium
- 2 cups capellini
- 2 teaspoons of sesame oil
- Freshly ground white pepper
- 1 teaspoon of rice wine vinegar

Directions:

Pour the broth in a saucepan over medium-high heat. Bring to a boil. Add the shrimp, bok choy, oil, and sauce. Allow to boil and turn the heat to low. Simmer for 5 minutes.

Add the water chestnuts, pepper, vinegar, tofu, capellini, and scallions. Cook for 5 minutes or until the capellini is barely tender. Serve while hot.

Nutrition:

- Calories: 205
- Carbs: 20g
- Fat: 9g
- Protein: 9g

Iceberg Lettuce and Mushrooms Salad

Preparation Time: 10 mins

Cooking Time: 20 mins

Servings: 4

Ingredients:

- 1 head, large iceberg lettuce, sliced into 6 equal wedges, retain a core, rinsed, spun-dried
- For the dressing
- 1 can, 15 oz. button mushroom stems and pieces, rinsed, drained well
- 1 cup Greek yogurt
- ¼ cup cottage cheese
- 2 Tbsp. Lemon juice, freshly squeezed
- ½ cup white wine vinegar
- ½ tsp. Black pepper
- ¼ tsp. green stevia

Directions:

Except for button mushrooms, combine all dressing ingredients in a bowl. Mix until creamy. If the dressing is too thick, add more vinegar. Fold in mushrooms. Divide into 6 equal portions.

Place 1 wedge of lettuce wedge on a plate. Top with 1 portion of the dressing

Nutrition:

- Calories: 15
- Carbs: 3g
- Fat: 0g
- Protein: 1g

Arugula with Gorgonzola Dressing

Preparation Time: 10 minutes

Cooking Time: 0 minutes

Servings: 4

Ingredients:

- 1 bunch of arugulas, cleaned
- 1 pear, sliced thinly
- 1 tablespoon fresh lemon juice
- 1 garlic clove, bruised

- 1/3 cup Gorgonzola cheese, crumbled
- 1/4 cup vegetable stock, reduced-sodium
- Freshly ground pepper
- 4 teaspoons olive oil
- 1 tablespoon of cider vinegar

Directions:

Put the pear slices and lemon juice in a bowl. Toss to coat. Arrange the pear slices, along with the arugula, on a platter.

In a bowl, combine the vinegar, oil, cheese, broth, pepper, and garlic. Leave for 5 minutes, remove the garlic. Put the dressing, then serve.

Nutrition:

- Calories: 145
- Carbs: 23g
- Fat: 4g
- Protein: 6g

Fusilli with Grape Tomatoes and Kale

Preparation Time: 15 minutes

Cooking Time: 15 minutes

Servings: 4

Ingredients:

- ¼ cup wholegrain fusilli, cooked according to package instructions
- 1 handful kale, sliced into bite-sized pieces
- ½ cup grape tomatoes, quartered
- 2 Tbsp. cooking liquid
- ½ Tbsp. olive oil
- ¼ cup leeks, thinly sliced
- 1 garlic clove, minced
- Pinch of sea salt
- Pinch of black pepper, to taste
- 1 tsp. roasted almonds, chopped
- pecorino cheese, grated, for sprinkling

Directions:

Pour oil into a saucepan set over high heat. Add in leeks and garlic. Turn down the heat and sauté until leeks are soft, about 2 minutes.

Add in kale and tomatoes. Stir until kale is wilted, about 4 minutes.

Except for cheese, add in remaining ingredients. Toss well to combine.

Place the pasta dish on a plate and sprinkle pecorino cheese on top. Serve.

Nutrition:

- Calories: 510
- Carbs: 42g
- Fat: 32g
- Protein: 16g

Rice and Chicken Pot

Preparation Time: 5 minutes

Cooking Time: 25 minutes

Servings: 4

Ingredients:

- 1 lb. free-range chicken breast, boneless, skinless
- ¼ cup of brown rice
- ¾ lb. mushrooms of choice, sliced
- 1 leek, chopped
- ¼ cup almonds, chopped
- 1 cup of water
- 1 Tbsp. olive oil
- 1 cup green beans
- ½ cup apple cider vinegar
- 2 Tbsp. all-purpose flour
- 1 cup milk, low fat
- ¼ cup Parmesan cheese, freshly grated
- ¼ cup sour cream
- Pinch of sea salt, add more if needed
- ground black pepper, to taste

Directions:

Pour brown rice into a pot. Add in water. Cover and bring to a boil. Lower the heat, then simmer for 30 minutes or until rice is cooked.

Meanwhile, in a skillet, add the chicken breast and pour just enough water to cover—season with salt. Boil the mixture, then reduce heat and allow to simmer for 10 minutes.

Shred the chicken. Set aside.

Warm the olive oil. Cook leeks until tender. Add in mushrooms.

Pour apple cider vinegar into the mixture. Sauté the mixture until the vinegar has evaporated. Add in flour and milk into the skillet. Sprinkle Parmesan cheese and add in sour cream. Season with black pepper.

Preheat the oven to 350 degrees F. lightly grease a casserole dish with oil.

Spread cooked rice in the casserole dish, then the shredded chicken and green beans on top. Add mushrooms and leeks sauce. Put almonds on top.

Bake within 20 minutes or until golden brown. Allow cooling before serving.

Nutrition:

- Calories: 401
- Carbs: 54g
- Fat: 12g
- Protein: 20g

Shiitake and Spinach Pattie

Preparation Time: 10 minutes

Cooking Time: 15 minutes

Servings: 8

Ingredients:

- 1 ½ cups shiitake mushrooms, minced
- 1 ½ cups spinach, chopped
- 3 garlic cloves, minced
- 2 onions, minced
- 4 tsp. olive oil
- 1 egg
- 1 ½ cups quinoa, cooked
- 1 ½ tsp. Italian seasoning
- 1/3 cup toasted sunflower seeds, ground
- 1/3 cup Pecorino cheese, grated

Directions:

Heat olive oil in a saucepan. Once hot, sauté shiitake mushrooms for 3 minutes or until lightly seared. Add in garlic and onion. Sauté for 2 minutes or until fragrant and translucent. Set aside.

In the same saucepan, heat the remaining olive oil. Add in spinach. Reduce heat, then simmer for 1 minute, drain and transfer to a strainer.

Chop spinach finely and add into the mushroom mixture. Add egg into the spinach mixture. Fold in cooked quinoa—season with Italian seasoning, then mix until well combined. Sprinkle sunflower seeds and cheese.

Divide the spinach mixture into patties—Cook patties within 5 minutes or until firm and golden brown. Serve with burger bread.

Nutrition:

- Calories: 43
- Carbs: 9g
- Fat: 0g
- Protein: 3g

Cabbage Orange Salad with Citrusy Vinaigrette

Preparation Time: 10 minutes

Cooking Time: 0 minutes

Servings: 8

Ingredients:

- 1 teaspoon orange zest, grated
- 2 tablespoons vegetable stock, reduced-sodium
- 1 teaspoon each cider vinegar
- 4 cups red cabbage, shredded
- 1 teaspoon lemon juice
- 1 fennel bulb, sliced thinly
- 1 teaspoon balsamic vinegar
- 1 teaspoon raspberry vinegar
- 2 tablespoons of fresh orange juice
- 2 oranges, peeled, cut into pieces
- 1 tablespoon of honey
- 1/4 teaspoon of salt
- Freshly ground pepper
- 4 teaspoons of olive oil

Directions:

Put lemon juice, orange zest, cider vinegar, salt and pepper, broth, oil, honey, orange juice, balsamic vinegar, and raspberry in a bowl and whisk.

Extract the oranges, fennel, and cabbage. Toss to coat.

Nutrition:

- Calories: 70
- Carbs: 14g
- Fat: 0g
- Protein: 1g

Lemon Buttery Shrimp Rice

Preparation Time: 15 minutes

Cooking Time: 10 minutes

Servings: 3

Ingredients:

- ¼ cup cooked wild rice
- ½ tsp. Butter divided
- ¼ tsp. olive oil
- 1 cup raw shrimps, shelled, deveined, drained
- ¼ cup frozen peas, thawed, rinsed, drained
- 1 Tbsp. lemon juice, freshly squeezed
- 1 Tbsp. chives, minced
- Pinch of sea salt, to taste

Directions:

Pour ¼ tsp. Butter and oil into wok set over medium heat. Add in shrimps and peas. Sauté until shrimps are coral pink, about 5 to 7 minutes.

Add in wild rice and cook until well heated—season with salt and butter.

Transfer to a plate. Sprinkle chives and lemon juice on top. Serve.

Nutrition:

- Calories: 510
- Carbs: 0g
- Fat: 0g
- Protein: 0g

Valencia Salad

Preparation Time: 10 minutes

Cooking Time: 0 minutes

Servings: 10

Ingredients:

- 1 tsp. Kalamata olives in oil, pitted, drained lightly, halved, julienned
- 1 head, small Romaine lettuce, rinsed, spun-dried, sliced into bite-sized pieces
- ½ piece, small shallot, julienned
- 1 tsp. Dijon mustard
- ½ small satsuma or tangerine, pulp only
- 1 tsp. white wine vinegar
- 1 tsp. extra virgin olive oil
- 1 pinch fresh thyme, minced
- Pinch of sea salt
- Pinch of black pepper, to taste

Directions:

Combine vinegar, oil, fresh thyme, salt, mustard, black pepper, and honey, if using. Whisk well until dressing emulsifies a little.

Toss together the remaining salad ingredients in a salad bowl.

Drizzle dressing on top when about to serve. Serve immediately with 1 slice if sugar-free sourdough bread or saltine.

Nutrition:

- Calories: 238
- Carbs: 23g
- Fat: 15g
- Protein: 8g

Tenderloin Stir Fry with Red and Green Grapes

Preparation Time: 15 minutes

Cooking Time: 25 minutes

Servings: 4

Ingredients:

- 1 medallion, 6 oz. pork tenderloin, trimmed well, remove the membrane
- sea salt
- sesame oil

- For grape vinaigrette
- ¼ cup green grapes, quartered
- ¼ cup red grapes, quartered
- black peppercorns, freshly cracked
- 1 tsp. apple cider vinegar, freshly juiced

Directions:

To make the vinaigrette, toss ingredients in a bowl. Chill before serving.

Meanwhile, preheat the stovetop or electric grill for at least 3 minutes.

Lightly season pork with salt and sesame oil. Grill only until well seared on both sides, about 10 to 12 minutes. Remove from grill. Cover with aluminum foil, then let the meat rest 5 minutes.

Place cooked pork medallion on a plate. Top off with vinaigrette. Serve.

Nutrition:

- Calories: 330
- Carbs: 28g
- Fat: 9g
- Protein: 27g

Aioli with Eggs

Preparation Time: 20 minutes

Cooking Time: 0 minutes

Servings: 12

Ingredients:

- 2 egg yolks
- 1 garlic, grated
- 2 Tbsp. water
- ½ cup extra virgin olive oil
- ¼ cup lemon juice, fresh squeezed, pips removed
- ¼ tsp. sea salt
- Dash of cayenne pepper powder
- Pinch of white pepper, to taste

Directions:

Pour garlic, egg yolks, salt, and water into blender; process until smooth. Put in olive oil in a slow stream until dressing emulsifies.

Add in remaining ingredients. Taste; adjust seasoning if needed. Pour into an airtight container; use as needed.

Nutrition:

- Calories: 100
- Carbs: 1g
- Fat: 11g
- Protein: 0g

Aioli on Spaghetti Squash

Preparation Time: 10 minutes

Cooking Time: 10 minutes

Servings: 4

Ingredients:

- 1 spaghetti squash, halved lengthwise, seeds scooped out
- ¼ cup Aioli with eggs
- olive oil for drizzling
- sea salt
- black pepper to taste

Directions:

Preheat oven to 375°F/190°C. Using a pastry brush, lightly grease the baking sheet with oil.

Drizzle more oil onto cut sides of squash, with a generous sprinkling of salt and pepper.

Place veggies cut side down on baking sheet; roast in a hot oven for 40 to 45 minutes or until squash is fork-tender.

Remove and cool. Flip squash over; fork through flesh to make spaghetti strands.

Place veggie noodles in a bowl; pour in ¼ cup of aioli. Toss gently to combine. Taste; drizzle in more aioli if desired. Season well with salt and pepper if desired; serve.

Nutrition:

- Calories: 31
- Carbs: 7g
- Fat: 1g
- Protein: 1g

Ginger Chicken Stew

Preparation Time: 10 minutes

Cooking Time: 20 minutes

Servings: 6

Ingredients:

- ¼ cup chicken thigh fillet, diced
- ¼ cup cooked egg noodles
- 1 unripe papaya, peeled, diced
- 1 cup chicken broth, low-sodium, low-fat
- 1 medallion ginger, peeled, crushed
- dash onion powder
- dash garlic powder, add more if desired
- 1 cup of water
- 1 tsp. fish sauce
- dash white pepper
- 1-piece, small bird's eye chili, minced

Directions:

Put all the fixing in a large Dutch oven set over high heat. Boil. Turn down heat to the lowest setting. Put the lid on.

Let the stew cook for 20 minutes or until papaya is fork-tender. Turn off heat. Consume as is, or with ½ cup of cooked rice. Serve warm.

Nutrition:

- Calories: 273
- Carbs: 15g
- Fat: 9g
- Protein: 33g

Taro Leaves in Coconut Sauce

Preparation Time: 10 minutes

Cooking Time: 20 minutes

Servings: 5

Ingredients:

- 4 cups dried taro leaves
- 2 cans of coconut cream, divided
- ¼ cup ground pork, 90% lean
- 1 tsp. shrimp paste
- 1 bird's eye chili, minced

Directions:

Except for 1 can of coconut cream, place all ingredients in a crockpot set at medium setting. Secure lid. Cook undisturbed for 3 to 3½ hours.

Pour the remaining can of coconut cream before turning off the heat. Stir and serve.

Nutrition:

- Calories: 264
- Carbs: 8g
- Fat: 24g
- Protein: 4g

Seared Herbed Salmon Steak

Preparation Time: 10 minutes

Cooking Time: 5 minutes

Servings: 4

Ingredients:

- 1 lb. salmon steak, rinsed 1/8 tsp cayenne pepper
- 1 tsp chili powder
- ½ tsp cumin
- 2 garlic cloves, minced
- 1 tablespoon olive oil
- ¾ tsp salt
- 1 tsp freshly ground black pepper

Directions:

Preheat the oven to 350 degrees F.

In a bowl, combine cayenne pepper, chili powder, cumin, salt, and black pepper. Set aside.

Drizzle in olive oil onto the salmon steak. Rub on both sides. Rub garlic and the prepared spice mixture. Let sit for 10 minutes.

After allowing the flavors to meld, prepare an ovenproof skillet. Heat the olive oil. Once hot, season the salmon for 4 minutes on both sides.

Transfer skillet inside the oven. Bake for 10 minutes. Serve.

Nutrition:

- Calories: 210
- Carbs: 0g
- Fat: 14g

- Protein: 19g

Smoked Salmon Salad

Preparation Time: 15 minutes

Cooking Time: 20 minutes

Servings: 4

Ingredients:

- 2 baby fennel bulbs, thinly sliced, some fronds reserved
- 1 tablespoon salted baby capers, rinsed, drained
- ½ cup natural yogurt
- 2 tablespoons parsley, chopped
- 1 tablespoon lemon juice, freshly squeezed
- 2 tablespoons fresh chives, chopped
- 1 tablespoon chopped fresh tarragon
- 180g sliced smoked salmon, low-salt
- ½ red onion, sliced thinly
- 1 teaspoon lemon rind, finely grated
- ½ cup French green lentils, rinsed
- 60g fresh baby spinach
- ½ avocado, sliced
- A pinch of caster sugar

Directions:

Put water in a large saucepan with water and boil over moderate heat. Once boiling; cook the lentils until tender, for 20 minutes; drain well.

In the meantime, heat a chargrill pan over high heat in advance. Spray the fennel slices with some oil & cook until tender, for 2 minutes per side.

Process the chives, parsley, yogurt, tarragon, lemon rind, and capers in a food processor until completely smooth and then season with pepper to taste.

Place the onion with sugar, juice & a pinch of salt in a large-sized mixing bowl. Set aside for a couple of minutes and then drain.

Combine the lentils with onion, fennel, avocado, and spinach in a large-sized mixing bowl. Evenly divide among the plates and then top with the fish. Sprinkle with the leftover fennel fronds & more of fresh parsley. Drizzle with the green goddess dressing. Enjoy.

Nutrition:

- kcal: 368
- Fat: 14 g
- Fiber: 8 g
- Protein: 20 g

Turkey Couscous Pilaf

Preparation Time: 20 minutes

Cooking Time: 20 minutes

Servings: 4

Ingredients:

- 1 ¼ pounds turkey mince
- ½ teaspoon ground cinnamon
- 1 small red onion, finely chopped
- ¼ teaspoon dried chili flakes
- 2 garlic cloves, crushed
- 1 lemon, juiced, rind finely grated
- 1 ½ teaspoon ground coriander
- ¾ teaspoon ground ginger
- 1 cup mint leaves, fresh, firmly packed
- 1 ½ teaspoon ground cumin
- 1 cup couscous
- ½ cup cranberries, dried
- 1 cup boiling water
- 2 tablespoons pistachios, toasted, chopped
- 1 cup coriander leaves, fresh, firmly packed
- Extra virgin olive oil, to serve

Directions:

Warm the oil until hot in a skillet. Once done, add & cook the onion with garlic until soft, frequently stirring for 2 minutes. Add the ground coriander, cumin, ginger, chili, and cinnamon. Continue to cook until aromatic, for a minute more, frequently stirring to prevent burning. Increase the heat to high and then add the turkey. Cook until cooked through and browned, for 6 more minutes. As you cook the meat; don't forget to break up the mince using a large wooden spoon

In the meantime, place the cranberries with couscous, lemon juice, rind & water in a heatproof bowl. Using a plastic wrap, cover & let stand for 5 minutes to absorb, fluff well using a large fork. Season to taste.

Finely chop half of the coriander and mint. Add the turkey mixture, coriander, and mint to the couscous. Mix well. Sprinkle with the pistachios & then drizzle with more of the oil.

Nutrition:

- kcal: 200
- Fat: 14 g
- Fiber: 3 g
- Protein: 34 g

Juicy Broccolini With Anchovy Almonds

Preparation Time: 10 minutes

Cooking Time: 10 minutes

Servings: 6

Ingredients:

- 2 bunches of broccolini, trimmed
- 1 tablespoon extra-virgin olive oil
- 1 long fresh red chili, deseeded, finely chopped
- 2 garlic cloves, thinly sliced
- ¼ cup natural almonds, coarsely chopped
- 2 teaspoons lemon rind, finely grated
- A squeeze of lemon juice, fresh
- 4 anchovies in oil, chopped

Directions:

Warm the oil until hot in a large saucepan. Add the drained anchovies, garlic, chili, and lemon rind. Cook until aromatic, for 30 seconds, stirring frequently. Add the almond & continue to cook for a minute more, stirring frequently. Remove from the heat & add a squeeze of fresh lemon juice.

Then place the broccolini in a steamer basket set over a saucepan of simmering water. Cover & cook until crisp-tender, for 2 to 3 minutes. Drain well and then transfer to a large-sized serving plate. Top with the almond mixture. Enjoy.

Nutrition:

- kcal: 350
- Fat: 7 g
- Fiber: 3 g
- Protein: 6 g

Amaranth and Quinoa Stuffed Peppers

Preparation Time: 20 minutes

Cooking Time: 1 hour & 10 minutes

Servings: 4

Ingredients:

- 2 tablespoons Amaranth
- 1 medium zucchini, trimmed, grated
- 2 vine-ripened tomatoes, diced
- 2/3 cup (approximately 135 g) quinoa
- 1 onion, medium-sized, chopped finely
- 2 crushed garlic cloves
- 1 teaspoon ground cumin
- 2 tablespoons lightly toasted sunflower seeds
- 75g ricotta cheese, fresh
- 2 tablespoons currants
- 4 capsicums, large, halved lengthwise & seeded
- 2 tablespoons flat-leaf parsley, roughly chopped

Directions:

Line a baking tray, preferably large-sized with some baking paper (nonstick) and then preheat your oven to 350 F in advance. Fill a medium-sized saucepan with an approximately a half-liter of water and then add the amaranth and quinoa; bring it to a boil over moderate heat. Once done, decrease the heat to low; cover & let simmer until grains turn al dente and water is absorbed, for 12 to 15 minutes. Remove from the heat & set aside.

In the meantime, lightly coat a large-sized frying pan with oil and heat it over medium heat. Once hot, add the onion with zucchini & cook until softened, for a couple of minutes, stirring frequently. Add the cumin and garlic; cook for a minute. Remove from the heat & set aside to cool.

Place the grains, onion mixture, sunflower seeds, currants, parsley, ricotta, and tomato in a mixing bowl, preferably large-sized; give the ingredients a good stir until combined well—season with pepper and salt to taste.

Fill the capsicums with prepared quinoa mixture & arrange them on the tray, covering the tray with aluminum foil—Bake for 17 to 20 minutes. Remove the foil & bake until the stuffing turns into golden & vegetables turn fork-tender, for 15 to 20 more minutes.

Nutrition:

- kcal: 200
- Fat: 8.5 g
- Fiber: 8 g
- Protein: 15 g

Barbecued Ocean Trout with Garlic and Parsley Dressing

Preparation Time: 20 minutes

Cooking Time: 25 minutes

Servings: 8

Ingredients:

- 3 ½ pounds piece of trout fillet, preferably ocean trout, boned, skin on
- 4 cloves of garlic, sliced thinly
- 2 tablespoons capers, coarsely chopped
- ½ cup flat-leaf parsley leaves, fresh
- 1 red chili, preferably long; sliced thinly
- 2 tablespoons lemon juice, freshly squeezed
- ½ cup olive oil
- Lemon wedges, to serve

Directions:

Brush the trout with approximately 2 tablespoons of oil; ensure that all sides are coated nicely. Preheat your barbecue over high heat, preferably with a closed hood. Decrease the heat to medium; place the coated trout on the barbecue plate, preferably on the skin-side. Cook until partially cooked and turn golden, for a couple of minutes. Carefully turn the trout; cook until cooked through, for 12 to 15 minutes, with the hood closed. Transfer the fillet to a large-sized serving platter.

In the meantime, heat the leftover oil; garlic over low heat in a small-sized saucepan until just heated through; garlic begins to change its color. Remove, then stir in the capers, lemon juice, chili Drizzle the trout with the prepared dressing and then sprinkle with the fresh parsley leaves. Immediately serve with fresh lemon wedges, enjoy.

Nutrition:

- kcal: 170
- Fat: 30 g
- Fiber: 2 g
- Protein: 37 g

Smashed Chickpea Avocado Salad Sandwich with Cranberries

Preparation Time: 10 minutes

Cooking Time: 10 minutes

Servings: 2

Ingredients:

- 4 slices of gluten-free bread
- 1 can chickpeas), rinsed & drained
- ground pepper & salt
- 2 teaspoon lemon juice, squeezed
- 1 large ripe avocado
- ¼ cup of cranberries, dried
- Arugula, spinach, or red onion to top

Directions:

Smash the chickpeas using a large fork in a medium-sized mixing bowl. Add in the avocado & smash again using the same fork until avocado is completely smooth; don't worry if it contains some chunky pieces.

Stir in the cranberries and lemon juice—season with pepper and salt to taste. Fridge until ready to serve.

Before serving, toast the bread and then spread approximately ½ of the chickpea avocado salad on one slice. Top with arugula, spinach, or red onion. Add another toasted piece on top and then cut in half. Serve immediately & enjoy.

Nutrition:

- kcal: 405
- Fat: 15 g

- Fiber: 17 g
- Protein: 12 g

Delicious Tuna Salad

Preparation Time: 10 minutes

Cooking Time: 15 minutes

Servings: 2

Ingredients:

- 2 cans tuna packed in water (5oz each), drained
- ¼ cup mayonnaise
- 2 tablespoons fresh basil, chopped
- 1 tablespoon lemon juice, freshly squeezed
- 2 tablespoons fire-roasted red peppers, chopped
- ¼ cup kalamata or mixed olives, chopped
- 2 large vine-ripened tomatoes
- 1 tablespoon capers
- 2 tablespoons red onion, minced
- Pepper & salt to taste

Directions:

Add all the items (except tomatoes) together in a large-sized mixing bowl; give the ingredients a good stir until combined well. Slice the tomatoes into sixths and then gently pry it open. Scoop the prepared tuna salad mixture into the middle; serve immediately & enjoy.

Nutrition:

- kcal: 405
- Fat: 24 g
- Fiber: 3.2 g
- Protein: 37 g

Turkey Chili

Preparation Time: 15 minutes

Cooking Time: 4 hours and 10 minutes

Servings: 8

Ingredients:

- 1-pound ground turkey, preferably 99% lean
- 2 cans of red kidney beans, rinsed & drained (15 oz each)
- 1 red pepper, chopped
- 2 cans of tomato sauce (15 oz each)
- 1 jar deli-sliced tamed jalapeno peppers, drained (16 oz)
- 2 cans of petite tomatoes, diced (15 oz each)
- 1 tablespoon cumin
- 1 yellow pepper, roughly chopped
- 2 cans of black beans, preferably rinsed & drained (15 oz each)
- 1 cup corn, frozen
- 2 tablespoon chili powder
- 1 tablespoon olive oil
- Black pepper & salt to taste
- 1 medium onion, diced
- Green onions, avocado, shredded cheese, Greek yogurt/sour cream, to top, optional

Directions:

Warm the oil until hot in a large skillet. Once done, carefully place the turkey into the hot skillet & cook until turn brown. Pour the turkey into the bottom of your slow cooker, preferably 6 quarts.

Add the jalapeños, corn, peppers, onion, diced tomatoes, tomato sauce, beans, cumin, and chili powder. Mix, then put pepper and salt to taste.

Cover & cook for 6 hours on low heat or 4 hours on high heat. Serve with the optional toppings and enjoy.

Nutrition:

- kcal: 455
- Fat: 9 g
- Fiber: 19 g
- Protein: 38 g

Kale Caesar Salad with Grilled Chicken Wrap

Preparation Time: 10 minutes

Cooking Time: 20 minutes

Servings: 2

Ingredients:

- 6 cups curly kale, cut into small, bite-sized pieces
- ½ coddled egg; cooked
- 8 ounces grilled chicken, thinly sliced
- ½ teaspoon Dijon mustard
- ¾ cup Parmesan cheese, finely shredded
- ground black pepper
- kosher salt
- 1 garlic clove, minced
- 1 cup cherry tomatoes, quartered
- 1/8 cup lemon juice, freshly squeezed
- 2 large tortillas or two Lavash flatbreads
- 1 teaspoon agave or honey
- 1/8 cup olive oil

Directions:

Combine half of the coddled egg with mustard, minced garlic, honey, olive oil, and lemon juice in a large-sized mixing bowl. Whisk until you get dressing like consistency. Season with pepper and salt to taste.

Add the cherry tomatoes, chicken and kale; gently toss until nicely coated with the dressing & then add ¼ cup of parmesan.

Spread out the flatbreads & evenly distribute the prepared salad on top of the wraps; sprinkle each with approximately ¼ cup of the parmesan.

Roll up the wraps & slice into half. Serve immediately & enjoy.

Nutrition:

- kcal: 511
- Fat: 29 g
- Fiber: 2.8 g
- Protein: 50 g

Baked Tilapia Recipe with Pecan Rosemary Topping

Preparation Time: 10 minutes

Cooking Time: 20 minutes

Servings: 4

Ingredients:

- 4 tilapia fillets (4 ounces each)
- ½ teaspoon brown sugar or coconut palm sugar
- 2 teaspoons fresh rosemary, chopped
- 1/3 cup raw pecans, chopped
- A pinch of cayenne pepper
- 1 ½ teaspoon olive oil
- 1 large egg white
- 1/8 teaspoon salt
- 1/3 cup panko breadcrumbs, preferably whole-wheat

Directions:

Heat-up your oven to 350 F.

Stir the pecans with breadcrumbs, coconut palm sugar, rosemary, cayenne pepper, and salt in a small-sized baking dish. Add the olive oil; toss.

Bake within 7 to 8 minutes, until the mixture turns light golden brown.

Adjust the heat to 400 F and coat a large-sized glass baking dish with some cooking spray.

Whisk the egg white in the shallow dish. Work in batches; dip the fish (one tilapia at a time) into the egg white, and then, coating lightly into the pecan mixture. Put the coated fillets in the baking dish.

Press the leftover pecan mixture over the tilapia fillets.

Bake within 8 to 10 minutes. Serve immediately & enjoy.

Nutrition:

- kcal: 222
- Fat: 10 g
- Fiber: 2 g
- Protein: 27 g

Clean Eating Egg Salad

Preparation Time: 10 minutes

Cooking Time: 0 minutes

Servings: 2

Ingredients:

- 6 organic pasture-raised eggs, hard-boiled
- 1 avocado
- ¼ cup of Greek yogurt

- 2 tablespoons of olive oil mayonnaise
- 1 teaspoon of fresh dill
- Sea salt to taste
- Lettuce for serving

Directions:

Mash the hard-boiled eggs and avocado together.

Add in the Greek yogurt, olive oil mayonnaise, and fresh dill.

Season with sea salt. Serve on a bed of lettuce.

Nutrition:

- Total Carbohydrates: 18g
- Dietary Fiber: 10g
- Protein: 23g
- Total Fat: 38g
- Calories: 486

Winter Style Fruit Salad

Preparation Time: 10 minutes

Cooking Time: 0 minutes

Servings: 6

Ingredients:

- 4 cooked sweet potatoes, cubed (1-inch cubes)
- 3 pears, cubed (1-inch cubes)
- 1 cup of grapes, halved
- 1 apple, cubed
- ½ cup of pecan halves
- 2 tablespoons of olive oil
- 1 tablespoon of red wine vinegar
- 2 tablespoons of raw honey

Directions:

Mix the olive oil, red wine vinegar, then the raw honey to make the dressing, and set aside.

Combine the chopped fruit, sweet potato, and pecan halves, and divide this between six serving bowls. Drizzle each bowl with the dressing.

Nutrition:

- Total Carbohydrates: 40g
- Dietary Fiber: 6g
- Protein: 3g
- Total Fat: 11g
- Calories: 251

Easy Salmon Salad

Preparation Time: 10 minutes

Cooking Time: 0 minutes

Servings: 1

Ingredients:

- 1 cup of organic arugula
- 1 can of wild-caught salmon
- ½ of an avocado, sliced
- 1 tablespoon of olive oil
- 1 teaspoon of Dijon mustard
- 1 teaspoon of sea salt

Directions:

Start by whisking the olive oil, Dijon mustard, and sea salt together in a mixing bowl to make the dressing. Set aside.

Assemble the salad with the arugula as the base, and top with the salmon and sliced avocado.

Drizzle with the dressing.

Nutrition:

- Total Carbohydrates: 7g
- Dietary Fiber: 5g
- Protein: 48g
- Total Fat: 37g
- Calories: 553

Healthy Pasta Salad

Preparation Time: 15 minutes

Cooking Time: 10 minutes

Servings: 6

Ingredients:

- 1 package of gluten-free fusilli pasta
- 1 cup of grape tomatoes, sliced
- 1 handful of fresh cilantro, chopped
- 1 cup of olives, halved
- 1 cup of fresh basil, chopped

- ½ cup of olive oil
- Sea salt to taste

Directions:

Whisk together the olive oil, chopped basil, cilantro, and sea salt. Set aside.

Cook the pasta according to package directions, strain, and rinse.

Combine the pasta with the tomatoes and olives.

Add the olive oil mixture, and toss until well combined.

Nutrition:

- Total Carbohydrates: 66g
- Dietary Fiber: 5g
- Protein: 13g
- Total Fat: 23g
- Calories: 525

Spinach Bean Salad

Preparation Time: 10 minutes

Cooking Time: 5 minutes

Servings: 1

Ingredients:

- 1 cup of fresh spinach
- ¼ cup of canned black beans
- ½ cup of canned garbanzo beans
- ½ cup of cremini mushrooms
- 2 tablespoons of organic balsamic vinaigrette
- 1 tablespoon of olive oil

Directions:

Cook the cremini mushrooms with the olive oil over low, medium heat for 5 minutes, until lightly browned.

Assemble the salad by adding the fresh spinach to a plate and topping it with the beans, mushrooms, and the balsamic vinaigrette.

Nutrition:

- Total Carbohydrates: 26gg
- Dietary Fiber: 8g
- Protein: 9g
- Total Fat: 15g
- Calories: 274

Kale Salad

Preparation Time: 10 minutes

Cooking Time: 0 minutes

Servings: 1

Ingredients:

- 1 cup of fresh kale
- ½ cup of blueberries
- ½ cup of pitted cherries halved
- ¼ cup of dried cranberries
- 1 tablespoon of sesame seeds
- 2 tablespoons of olive oil
- Juice of 1 lemon

Directions:

Combine the olive oil and lemon juice, then toss the kale in the dressing.

Put the kale leaves into a salad bowl, and top with the fresh blueberries, cherries, and cranberries.

Top with the sesame seeds.

Nutrition:

- Total Carbohydrates: 48g
- Dietary Fiber: 7g
- Protein: 6g
- Total Fat: 33g
- Calories: 477

Sweet Potato Soup

Preparation Time: 15 minutes

Cooking Time: 15 minutes

Servings: 6

Ingredients:

- 2 tablespoons of olive oil
- 1 medium onion, chopped
- 1 can of green chilies
- 1 teaspoon of ground cumin
- 1 teaspoon of ground ginger
- 1 teaspoon of sea salt

- 4 cups of sweet potatoes, peeled and chopped
- 4 cups of organic, low-sodium vegetable broth
- 2 tablespoons of fresh cilantro, minced
- 6 tablespoons of Greek yogurt

Directions:

Heat-up the olive oil over medium heat in a large soup pot. Add in the onion, and sauté until soft. Add in the green chilies and seasonings, and cook for 2 minutes.

Stir in the sweet potatoes and vegetable broth, and bring to a boil.

Simmer within 15 minutes.

Stir in the minced cilantro.

Blend half of the soup until smooth. Put it back to the pot with the remaining soup.

Season with extra sea salt if desired, and top with a dollop of Greek yogurt.

Nutrition:

- Total Carbohydrates: 33g
- Dietary Fiber: 5g
- Protein: 6g
- Total Fat: 5g
- Calories: 192

Curry Lentil Stew

Preparation Time: 10 minutes

Cooking Time: 15 minutes

Servings: 4

Ingredients:

- 1 tablespoon of olive oil
- 1 onion, chopped
- 2 garlic cloves, minced
- 1 tablespoon of organic curry seasoning
- 4 cups of organic low-sodium vegetable broth
- 1 cup of red lentils
- 2 cups of butternut squash, cooked
- 1 cup of kale
- 1 teaspoon of turmeric
- Sea salt to taste

Directions:

Sauté the olive oil with the onion and garlic in a large pot over medium heat, add. Sauté for 3 minutes.

Add in the organic curry seasoning, vegetable broth, and lentils, and bring to a boil—Cook for 10 minutes.

Stir in the cooked butternut squash and kale.

Add in the turmeric and sea salt to taste.

Serve warm.

Nutrition:

- Total Carbohydrates: 41g
- Dietary Fiber: 13g
- Protein: 16g
- Total Fat: 4g
- Calories: 252

Black Bean Tortilla Wrap

Preparation Time: 10 minutes

Cooking Time: 0 minutes

Servings: 2

Ingredients:

- ¼ cup of corn
- 1 handful of fresh basil
- ½ cup of arugula
- 1 tablespoon of nutritional yeast
- ¼ cup of canned black beans
- 1 peach, sliced
- 1 teaspoon of lime juice
- 2 gluten-free tortillas

Directions:

Divide the beans, corn, arugula, and peaches between the two tortillas.

Top each tortilla with half the fresh basil and lime juice

Nutrition:

- Total Carbohydrates: 44g
- Dietary Fiber: 7g
- Protein: 8g

- Total Fat: 1g
- Calories: 203

Sweet Potato Patties

Preparation Time: 10 minutes

Cooking Time: 5 minutes

Servings: 4

Ingredients:

- 2 ½ cups of sweet potato, peeled & shredded
- 1/3 cup of rice flour
- ½ cup of white onion, chopped
- 1 large organic pasture-raised egg, beaten
- 12 tablespoons coconut oil for cooking
- Salt and pepper to taste

Directions:

Combine the sweet potato and flour in a large mixing bowl, and stir. Add the onion and egg, and mix all.

Divide the sweet potato mixture into four balls and form each one into a small patty.

Add 12 tablespoons of coconut oil to a pan over medium heat and allow to melt,

Cook each patty for 3 minutes, or until they are golden brown, on each side.

Serve with a side salad for the perfect anti-inflammatory lunch.

Nutrition:

- Total Carbohydrates: 72g
- Dietary Fiber: 10g
- Protein: 8g
- Total Fat: 5g
- Calories: 359

Coconut Mushroom Soup

Preparation Time: 10 minutes

Cooking Time: 10 minutes

Servings: 3

Ingredients:

- 1 tablespoon of coconut oil
- 1 tablespoon of ground ginger
- 1 cup of cremini mushrooms, chopped
- ½ teaspoon of turmeric
- 2 and ½ cups of water
- ½ cup of canned coconut milk
- Sea salt to taste

Directions:

Heat-up the coconut oil over medium heat in a large pot, and add the mushrooms. Cook for 3-4 minutes.

Put the remaining fixings and boil. Let it simmer for 5 minutes.

Divide between three soup bowls, and enjoy!

Nutrition:

- Total Carbohydrates: 4g
- Dietary Fiber: 1g
- Protein: 2g
- Total Fat: 14g
- Calories: 143

Tomato Detox Soup

Preparation Time: 10 minutes

Cooking Time: 20 minutes

Servings: 2

Ingredients:

- ½ cup of organic, low-sodium vegetable stock
- 1 can dice organic tomatoes
- 2 teaspoons of turmeric
- 1 teaspoon of olive oil
- 2 cloves of garlic
- 1 small onion, chopped
- 1 handful of fresh basil

Directions:

Put all of the fixings into a large stockpot, and bring to a boil.

Simmer for 20 minutes.

With an immersion blender, blend until smooth.

Serve with a slice of gluten-free toast or a side salad.

Nutrition:

- Total Carbohydrates: 14g
- Dietary Fiber: 5g
- Protein: 3g
- Total Fat: 3g
- Calories: 86

Cauliflower Soup

Preparation Time: 5 minutes

Cooking Time: 10 minutes

Servings: 10

Ingredients:

- ¾ cup of water
- 2 teaspoon of olive oil
- 1 onion, diced
- 1 head of cauliflower, only the florets
- 1 can of full-fat coconut milk
- 1 teaspoon of turmeric
- 1 teaspoon of ginger
- 1 teaspoon raw honey

Directions:

Put all of the fixings into a large stockpot, and boil for about 10 minutes.

Use an immersion blender to blend and make the soup smooth. Serve.

Nutrition:

- Total Carbohydrates: 7g
- Dietary Fiber: 2g
- Net Carbs:
- Protein: 2g
- Total Fat: 11g
- Calories: 129

Bean Shawarma Salad

Preparation Time: 15 minutes

Cooking Time: 20 minutes

Servings: 2

Ingredients:

For Preparing Salad

- 20 Pita chips
- 5-ounces Spring lettuce
- 10 Cherry tomatoes
- ¾ Cup fresh parsley
- ¼ Cup red onion (chop)

For Chickpeas

- 1tbsp Olive oil
- 1 Heading-tbsp cumin and turmeric
- ½ Heading-tbsp paprika and coriander powder
- 1 Pinch black pepper
- ½ Scant Kosher salt
- ¼tbsp Ginger and cinnamon powder

For Preparing Dressing

- 3 Garlic Cloves
- 1tbsp Dried drill
- 1tbsp Lime juice
- Water
- ½ Cup hummus

Directions:

Place a rack in the already preheated oven (204C). Mix chickpeas with all spices and herbs.

Place a thin layer of chickpeas on the baking sheet and bake it almost for 20 minutes. Bake it until the beans are golden brown.

For preparing the dressing, mix all ingredients in a whisking bowl and blend it. Add water gradually for appropriate smoothness.

Mix all herbs and spices for preparing salad.

For serving, add pita chips and beans in the salad and drizzle some dressing over it.

Nutrition:

- Calories: 173
- Carbs: 8g
- Fat: 6g
- Protein: 19g

Pesto Pasta with Walnut Sage & Delicious Squash

Preparation Time: 15 minutes

Cooking Time: 25 minutes

Servings: 6

Ingredients:

For Roasted Squash

- 2 Squash medium-sized
- 2tbsp extra-virgin olive oil
- Salt-to-taste
- Fresh Black Pepper

For Preparing Pasta

- 1lb of boiled penne
- 4tbsp Olive oil
- Some fresh sage leaves
- ½ Cup of parmigiana-Reggiano gritted cheese

For Preparing Walnut Sage Pesto

- 3 Garlic cloves
- 6 Parsley & 7-8 sage leaves
- Fresh black pepper
- Salt-to-taste
- ½ cup walnut oil
- ¾ Cup of walnuts

Directions:

Preheat the oven at 240C. Boil pasta in a large pot.

Place moon slices of squash on the baking sheet and drizzle salt and pepper on it. Roast it in the oven almost for 20 mins.

Prepare walnut sage pesto by combining walnuts, sage & parsley leaves, salt, pepper, and garlic cloves and blend it.

Add walnut oil gradually in the blender and make a smooth sauce.

Line up roasted squash in a plate with some boil penne and walnut sauce.

Nutrition:

- Calories: 325
- Carbs: 52g
- Fat: 11g
- Protein: 9g

Feta Frittata & Spinach

Preparation Time: 15 minutes

Cooking Time: 10 minutes

Servings: 4

Ingredients:

- ½ small brown onion
- 250g baby spinach
- ½ cup feta cheese
- 1 tbsp garlic paste
- 4 beaten eggs

Seasoning Mix

- Salt & Pepper according to taste
- 1 tbsp olive oil

Directions:

Add finely chop an onion in oil and cook it on medium flame.

Add spinach in light brown onions and toss it for 2 min.

In eggs, add the mixture of cold spinach and onions.

Now add garlic paste, salt, and pepper and mix the mixture.

Cook this mixture on low flame and stir eggs gently.

Add feta cheese on the eggs and place the pan under the already preheat grill.

Cook it almost for 2 to 3 minutes until the frittata is brown.

Serve this feta frittata hot or cold.

Nutrition:

- Calories: 210
- Carbs: 5g
- Fat: 14g
- Protein: 21g

Coconut Green Curry with Boil Rice

Preparation Time: 15 minutes

Cooking Time: 20 minutes

Servings: 8

Ingredients:

- 2tbsp Olive oil
- 12ounces of Tofu
- 2 medium sweet potatoes (cut into cubes)
- Salt-to-taste
- 314ounces Coconut milk
- 4tbsp Green curry paste
- 3 Cups of Broccoli Florets

Directions:

Remove excess water from tofu and fry it on medium flame. Add salt in it and fry it for 12 minutes.

Cook coconut milk, green curry paste, and sweet potato on medium heat and simmer it for 5 mins.

Now add broccoli and tofu in it and cook it almost 5 minutes until the broccoli color changes.

Serve this coconut and green curry with a handful of boil rice and many raisins on top of it.

Nutrition:

- Calories: 170
- Carbs: 34g
- Fat: 2g
- Protein: 3g

Chicken Salad with Chinese Touch

Preparation Time: 15 minutes

Cooking Time: 25 minutes

Servings: 3

Ingredients:

- 1 Medium green onion (thinly sliced)
- 2 Boneless chicken breasts
- 2tbsp Soya sauce
- ¼ Teaspoon white pepper
- 1tbsp sesame oil
- 4 cups romaine lettuce (chopped)
- 1 cup cabbage (shredded)
- ¼ Cup small cubes carrots
- ¼ Cup thin sliced almonds
- ¼ Cup noodles (only for serving)

For Preparing Chinese Dressing:

- 1 Minced garlic clove
- 1 Teaspoon soy sauce
- 1tbsp sesame oil
- 2tbsp Rice vinegar
- 1tbsp Sugar

Directions:

Prepare Chinese dressing by whisking all ingredients in a bowl.

In a bowl, marinate chicken breasts with garlic, olive oil, soy sauce, and white pepper for 20 minutes.

Place baking dish in the preheated oven (at 225C).

Place chicken breasts in the baking dish and bake it almost for 20 minutes.

For assembling the salad, combine romaine lettuce, cabbage, carrots, and green onion.

For serving, place a chicken piece in a plate and salad on top of it. Pour some dressing over it alongside noodles.

Nutrition:

- Calories: 130
- Carbs: 10g
- Fat: 6g
- Protein: 10g

Lentil Soup with Spices

Preparation Time: 15 minutes

Cooking Time: 25 minutes

Servings: 5

Ingredients:

- 1 Cup of yellow onion (cut into cubes)
- 1 Cup of carrot (cut into cubes)

- 1 Cup of turnip
- 2tbsp extra-virgin olive oil
- 2tbsp balsamic vinegar
- 4 cups of baby spinach
- 2 cups brown lentils
- ¼ Cup of fresh parsley

Directions:

Preheat the pressure cooker on medium flame and add olive oil and vegetables in it.

After 5 minutes, add broth, lentils, and salt in the pot and simmer for 15 minutes.

Remove the lid and add spinach and vinegar in it.

Stir the soup for 5 minutes and turn off the flame.

Garnish it with fresh parsley.

Nutrition:

- Calories: 96
- Carbs: 16g
- Fat: 1g
- Protein: 4g

Baked Sweet Potato with Red Tahini Sauce

Preparation Time: 15 minutes

Cooking Time: 30 minutes

Servings: 4

Ingredients:

- 15-ounces Canned Chickpeas
- 4 Medium-sized sweet potatoes
- ½ tbsp Olive oil
- 1 Pinch salt
- 1tbsp Lime juice
- 1/2 tbsp of cumin, coriander, and paprika powder

For Garlic Herb Sauce

- ¼ Cup tahini sauce
- ½ tbsp Lime Juice
- 3 cloves garlic
- Salt to taste

Directions:

Preheat the oven at 204°C. Toss chickpeas in salt, spices & olive oil. Spread them on the foil sheet.

Brush sweet potato thin wedges with oil and place them on marinated beans and bake.

For the sauce, mix all fixings in a bowl. Add some water in it, but keep it thick.

Remove sweet potatoes from the oven after 25 minutes.

Garnish this baked sweet potato chickpea salad with hot garlic sauce.

Nutrition:

- Calories: 90
- Carbs: 20g
- Fat: 0g
- Protein: 2g

Bake chicken Top-up with Olives, Tomatoes, and Basil

Preparation Time: 15 minutes

Cooking Time: 45 minutes

Servings: 4

Ingredients:

- 8 Chicken thighs
- Small Italian tomatoes
- 1tbsp Black pepper & salt
- 1tbsp Olive oil
- 15 Basil leaves (large)
- Small black olives
- 1-2 Fresh red chili flakes

Directions:

Marinate chicken pieces with all spices & olive oil and leave it for some time.

Assemble chicken pieces in a rimmed pan with top-up with tomatoes, basil leaves, olives, and chili flakes.

Bake this chicken in an already preheated oven (at 220C) for 40 minutes.

Bake until the chicken is tender, tomatoes, basil, and olives are cooked.

Garnish it with fresh parsley and lemon zest.

Nutrition:

- Calories: 304
- Carbs: 18g
- Fat: 7g
- Protein: 41g

Sweet Potato & Chicken Soup with Lentil

Preparation Time: 15 minutes

Cooking Time: 35 minutes

Servings: 6

Ingredients:

- 10 Celery stalks
- 1 Home-cooked or rotisserie chicken
- 2 medium sweet potatoes
- 5-ounces French lentils
- 2tbsp Fresh lime juice
- ½ head bite-size escarole
- 6 thin-sliced garlic cloves
- ½ Cup dill (finely chop)
- 1tbsp Kosher Salt
- 2tbsp Extra virgin oil

Directions:

Add salt, chicken carcass, lentil, and sweet potatoes in 8 ounces of water and boil it on high flame.

Cook these items almost for 10-12 minutes and skim off all the foam form on it.

Cook garlic and celery in oil almost for 10 minutes until it is tender & light brown, then add shredded roast chicken in it.

Add this mixture in the escarole soup and continuously stir it for 5 minutes on medium heat.

Add lemon juice and stir in dill. Serve season hot soup with salt.

Nutrition:

- Calories: 310
- Carbs: 45g
- Fat: 11g
- Protein: 13g

White Bean Chicken with Winter Green Vegetables

Preparation Time: 15 minutes

Cooking Time: 45 minutes

Servings: 8

Ingredients:

- 4 Garlic cloves
- 1tbsp Olive oil
- 3 medium parsnips
- 1kg Small cubes of chicken
- 1 Teaspoon cumin powder
- 2 Leaks & 1 Green part
- 2 Carrots (cut into cubes)
- 1 ¼ White kidney beans (overnight soaked)
- ½ Teaspoon dried oregano
- 2 Teaspoon Kosher salt
- Cilantro leaves
- 1 1/2tbsp Ground ancho chilies

Directions:

Cook garlic, leeks, chicken, and olive oil in a large pot on a medium flame for 5 minutes.

Now add carrots and parsnips, and after stirring for 2 minutes, add all seasoning ingredients.

Stir until the fragrant starts coming from it.

Now add beans and 5 cups of water in the pot.

Bring it to a boil and reduce the flame.

Allow it to simmer almost for 30 minutes and garnish with parsley and cilantro leaves.

Nutrition:

- Calories: 263
- Carbs: 24g
- Fat: 7g
- Protein: 26g

Garlic Shrimps with Gritted Cauliflower

Preparation Time: 15 minutes

Cooking Time: 15 minutes

Servings: 2

Ingredients:

For Preparing Shrimps

- 1 Pound Shrimps
- 2-3tbsp Cajun seasoning
- Salt
- 1tbsp Butter/Ghee

For Preparing Cauliflower Grits

- 2tbsp Ghee
- 12-Ounces of Cauliflower
- 1 Garlic clove
- Salt-to-taste

Directions:

Boil cauliflower and garlic in 8ounces of water on medium flame until it's tender.

Blend tender cauliflower in the food processor with ghee. Add steaming water gradually for the right consistency.

Sprinkle 2tbsp of Cajun seasoning on shrimps and marinate.

In a large skillet, take 3tbsp of ghee and cook shrimps on medium flame.

Place a large spoon of cauliflower grits in bowl top up with fried shrimps.

Nutrition:

- Calories: 107
- Carbs: 1g
- Fat: 3g
- Protein: 20g

Garlic & Squash Noodles

Preparation Time: 15 minutes

Cooking Time: 15 minutes

Servings: 4

Ingredients:

For Preparing Sauce

- ¼ Cup coconut milk
- 6 Large dates
- 2/3g Gritted coconut
- 6 Garlic cloves
- 2tbsp Ginger paste
- 2tbsp Red curry paste

For Preparing Noodles

- 1 Large boil squash noodles
- ½ Julienne cut carrots
- ½ Julienne cut zucchini
- 1 small red bell pepper
- ¼ Cup cashew nuts

Directions:

For making sauce, blend all the ingredients and make a thick puree.

Cut spaghetti squash lengthwise and make noodles.

Lightly brush the baking tray with olive oil and bake squash noodles at 40C for 5-6 minutes.

For serving, incorporate noodles and puree in a bowl. Or serve puree alongside the noodles.

Nutrition:

- Calories: 405
- Carbs: 107g
- Fat: 28g
- Protein: 7g

Garlic Chicken Bake with Basil &Tomatoes

Preparation Time: 15 minutes

Cooking Time: 30 minutes

Servings: 4

Ingredients:

- ½ medium yellow onion
- 2tbsp Olive oil
- 3 Minced Garlic Cloves
- 1 Cup Basil (loosely cut)
- 1.lb Boneless chicken breast
- 14.5-ounces Italian chop tomatoes
- Salt & pepper
- 4 Medium zucchinis (spiralized into noodles)
- 1tbsp crushed red pepper
- 2tbsp Olive oil

Directions:

Pound the chicken pieces with a pan for fast cooking. Sprinkle salt, pepper, and oil on chicken pieces and marinate both sides of chicken equally.

Fry chicken pieces on a large hot skillet for 2-3 minutes on each side.

Sautee onion in the same skillet pan until it's brown. Add tomatoes, basil leaves, and garlic in it.

Simmer it for 3 minutes and add all spices and chicken in the skillet.

Serve it on the plate along with saucy zoodles.

Nutrition:

- Calories: 44
- Carbs: 7g
- Fat: 0g
- Protein: 2g

Smoked Trout Wrapped in Lettuce

Preparation Time: 15 minutes

Cooking Time: 45 minutes

Servings: 4

Ingredients:

- ¼ Cup salt-roasted potatoes
- 1 cup grape tomatoes
- ½ Cup basil leaves
- 16 small & medium size lettuce leaves
- 1/3 cup Asian sweet chili
- 2 Carrots
- 1/3 Cup Shallots (thin sliced)
- ¼ Cup thin slice Jalapenos
- 1tbsp Sugar
- 2-4.5 Ounces skinless smoked trout
- 2tbsp Fresh lime Juice
- 1 Cucumber

Directions:

Cut carrots and cucumber in slim strip size.

Marinate these vegetables for 20 mins with sugar, fish sauce, lime juice, shallots, and jalapeno.

Add trout pieces and other herbs in this vegetable mixture and blend.

Strain water from vegetable and trout mixture and again toss it to blend.

Place lettuce leaves on a plate and transfer trout salad on them.

Garnish this salad with peanuts and chili sauce.

Nutrition:

- Calories: 180
- Carbs: 0g
- Fat: 12g
- Protein: 18g

Crusted Salmon with Walnuts & Rosemary

Preparation Time: 15 minutes

Cooking Time: 20 minutes

Servings: 6

Ingredients:

- 1 Mince garlic clove
- 1tbsp Dijon mustard
- ¼ tbsp Lemon zest
- 1tbsp Lemon juice
- 1tbsp fresh rosemary
- 1/2 tbsp Honey
- Olive oil
- Fresh parsley
- 3tbsp Chopped walnuts
- 1 Pound skinless salmon
- 1tbsp Fresh crushed red pepper
- Salt & pepper
- Lemon wedges for garnish
- 3tbsp Panko breadcrumbs
- 1tbsp extra-virgin olive oil

Directions:

Spread the baking sheet in the oven and preheat it at 240C.

In a bowl, mix mustard paste, garlic, salt, olive oil, honey, lemon juice, crushed red pepper, rosemary, pus honey.

Combine panko, walnuts, and oil and spread thin fish slice on the baking sheet. Spray olive oil equally on both sides of the fish.

Place walnut mixture on the salmon with the mustard mixture on top it.

Bake the salmon almost for 12 minutes. Garnish it with fresh parsley and lemon wedges and serve it hot.

Nutrition:

- Calories: 227
- Carbs: 0g
- Fat: 12g
- Protein: 29g

CHAPTER 11:

Dinner

Roasted Vegetables with Sweet Potatoes and White Beans

Preparation Time: 15 minutes

Cooking Time: 25 minutes

Servings: 4

Ingredients:

- 2 small sweet potatoes, dice
- ½ red onion, cut into ¼-inch dice
- 1 medium carrot, peeled and thinly sliced
- 4 ounces green beans, trimmed
- ¼ cup extra-virgin olive oil
- 1 teaspoon salt
- ¼ teaspoon freshly ground black pepper
- 1 (15½-ounce) can white beans, drained and rinsed
- 1 tablespoon minced or grated lemon zest
- 1 tablespoon chopped fresh dill

Directions:

Preheat the oven to 400°F.

Combine the sweet potatoes, onion, carrot, green beans, oil, salt, and pepper on a large rimmed baking sheet and mix to combine well. Arrange in a single layer.

Roast until the vegetables are tender, 20 to 25 minutes.

Add the white beans, lemon zest, and dill, mix well and serve.

Nutrition:

- Calories: 315
- Total Fat: 13g
- Total Carbohydrates: 42g
- Sugar: 5g
- Fiber: 13g
- Protein: 10g
- Sodium: 632mg

Roasted Tofu and Greens

Preparation Time: 10 minutes

Cooking Time: 20 minutes

Servings: 4

Ingredients:

- 3 cups baby spinach or kale
- 1 tablespoon sesame oil
- 1 tablespoon ginger, minced
- 1 garlic clove, minced
- 1-pound firm tofu, cut into 1-inch dice
- 1 tablespoon gluten-free tamari or soy sauce
- ¼ teaspoon red pepper flakes (optional)
- 1 teaspoon rice vinegar
- 2 scallions, thinly sliced

Directions:

Preheat the oven to 400°F.

Combine the spinach, oil, ginger, and garlic on a large rimmed baking sheet.

Bake until the spinach has wilted, 3 to 5 minutes.

Add the tofu, tamari, and red pepper flakes (if using) and toss to combine well.

Bake until the tofu is beginning to brown, 10 to 15 minutes.

Top with the vinegar and scallions and serve.

Nutrition:

- Calories: 121
- Total Fat: 8g
- Total Carbohydrates: 4g
- Sugar: 1g
- Fiber: 2g
- Protein: 10g
- Sodium: 258mg

Tofu and Italian-Seasoned Summer Vegetables

Preparation Time: 10 minutes

Cooking Time: 20 minutes

Servings: 4

Ingredients:

- 2 large zucchinis, cut into ¼-inch slices
- 2 large summer squash, cut into ¼-inch-thick slices
- 1-pound firm tofu, cut into 1-inch dice
- 1 cup vegetable broth or water
- 3 tablespoons extra-virgin olive oil
- 2 garlic cloves, sliced
- 1 teaspoon salt
- 1 teaspoon Italian herb seasoning blend
- ¼ teaspoon freshly ground black pepper
- 1 tablespoon thinly sliced fresh basil

Directions:

Preheat the oven to 400°F.

Combine the zucchini, squash, tofu, broth, oil, garlic, salt, Italian herb seasoning blend, and pepper on a large rimmed baking sheet, and mix well.

Roast within 20 minutes.

Sprinkle with the basil and serve.

Nutrition:

- Calories: 213
- Total Fat: 16g
- Total Carbohydrates: 9g
- Sugar: 4g
- Fiber: 3g
- Protein: 13g
- Sodium: 806mg

Spiced Broccoli, Cauliflower, And Tofu with Red Onion

Preparation Time: 10 minutes

Cooking Time: 25 minutes

Servings: 2

Ingredients:

- 2 cups broccoli florets
- 2 cups cauliflower florets
- 1 medium red onion, diced
- 3 tablespoons extra-virgin olive oil
- 1 teaspoon salt
- ¼ teaspoon freshly ground black pepper
- 1-pound firm tofu, cut into 1-inch dice
- 1 garlic clove, minced
- 1 (¼-inch) piece fresh ginger, minced

Directions:

Preheat the oven to 400°F.

Combine the broccoli, cauliflower, onion, oil, salt, and pepper on a large rimmed baking sheet, and mix well.

Roast until the vegetables have softened, 10 to 15 minutes.

Add the tofu, garlic, and ginger. Roast within 10 minutes.

Gently mix the ingredients on the baking sheet to combine the tofu with the vegetables and serve.

Nutrition:

- Calories: 210
- Total Fat: 15g
- Total Carbohydrates: 11g
- Sugar: 4g
- Fiber: 4g
- Protein: 12g
- Sodium: 626mg

Tempeh and Root Vegetable Bake

Preparation Time: 10 minutes

Cooking Time: 30 minutes

Servings: 4

Ingredients:

- 1 tablespoon extra-virgin olive oil
- 1 large sweet potato, dice
- 2 carrots, thinly sliced

- 1 fennel bulb, trimmed and cut into ¼-inch dice
- 2 teaspoons minced fresh ginger
- 1 garlic clove, minced
- 12 ounces tempeh, cut into ½-inch dice
- ½ cup vegetable broth
- 1 tablespoon gluten-free tamari or soy sauce
- 2 scallions, thinly sliced

Directions:

Preheat the oven to 400°F. Grease a baking sheet with the oil.

Arrange the sweet potato, carrots, fennel, ginger, and garlic in a single layer on the baking sheet.

Bake until the vegetables have softened, about 15 minutes.

Add the tempeh, broth, and tamari.

Bake again until the tempeh is heated through and lightly browned 10 to 15 minutes.

Add the scallions, mix well, and serve.

Nutrition:

- Calories: 276
- Total Fat: 13g
- Total Carbohydrates: 26g
- Sugar: 5g
- Fiber: 4g
- Protein: 19g
- Sodium: 397mg

Garlicky Chicken and Vegetables

Preparation Time: 10 minutes

Cooking Time: 45 minutes

Servings: 4

Ingredients:

- 2 teaspoons extra-virgin olive oil
- 1 leek, white part only, thinly sliced
- 2 large zucchinis, cut into ¼-inch slices
- 4 bone-in, skin-on chicken breasts
- 3 garlic cloves, minced
- 1 teaspoon salt
- 1 teaspoon dried oregano
- ¼ teaspoon freshly ground black pepper
- ½ cup white wine
- Juice of 1 lemon

Directions:

Preheat the oven to 400°F. Grease the baking sheet with the oil.

Place the leek and zucchini on the baking sheet.

Put the chicken, skin-side up, and sprinkle with the garlic, salt, oregano, and pepper. Add the wine.

Roast within 35 to 40 minutes. Remove and let rest for 5 minutes.

Add the lemon juice and serve.

Nutrition:

- Calories: 315
- Total Fat: 8g
- Total Carbohydrates: 12g
- Sugar: 4g
- Fiber: 2g
- Protein: 44g
- Sodium: 685mg

Turmeric-Spiced Sweet Potatoes, Apple, And Onion with Chicken

Preparation Time: 15 minutes

Cooking Time: 45 minutes

Servings: 4

Ingredients:

- 2 tablespoons unsalted butter, at room temperature
- 2 medium sweet potatoes
- 1 large Granny Smith apple
- 1 medium onion, thinly sliced
- 4 bone-in, skin-on chicken breasts
- 1 teaspoon salt
- 1 teaspoon turmeric
- 1 teaspoon dried sage
- ¼ teaspoon freshly ground black pepper

- 1 cup apple cider, white wine, or chicken broth

Directions:

Preheat the oven to 400°F. Grease the baking sheet with the butter.

Arrange the sweet potatoes, apple, and onion in a single layer on the baking sheet.

Put the chicken, skin-side up, and season with the salt, turmeric, sage, and pepper. Add the cider.

Roast within 35 to 40 minutes. Remove, let it rest for 5 minutes and serve.

Nutrition:

- Calories: 386
- Total Fat: 12g
- Total Carbohydrates: 26g
- Sugar: 10g
- Fiber: 4g
- Protein: 44g
- Sodium: 932mg

Honey-Roasted Chicken Thighs with Carrots

Preparation Time: 10 minutes

Cooking Time: 50 minutes

Servings: 4

Ingredients:

- 2 tablespoons unsalted butter, at room temperature
- 3 large carrots, thinly sliced
- 2 garlic cloves, minced
- 4 bone-in, skin-on chicken thighs
- 1 teaspoon salt
- ½ teaspoon dried rosemary
- ¼ teaspoon freshly ground black pepper
- 2 tablespoons honey
- 1 cup chicken broth or vegetable broth
- Lemon wedges, for serving

Directions:

Preheat the oven to 400°F. Grease the baking sheet with the butter.

Arrange the carrots and garlic in a single layer on the baking sheet.

Put the chicken, skin-side up, on top of the vegetables, and season with the salt, rosemary, and pepper.

Put the honey on top and add the broth.

Roast within 40 to 45 minutes. Remove, then let it rest for 5 minutes, and serve with lemon wedges.

Nutrition:

- Calories: 428
- Total Fat: 28g
- Total Carbohydrates: 15g
- Sugar: 11g
- Fiber: 2g
- Protein: 30g
- Sodium: 732mg

Sesame-Tamari Baked Chicken with Green Beans

Preparation Time: 10 minutes

Cooking Time: 45 minutes

Servings: 4

Ingredients:

- 1-pound green beans, trimmed
- 4 bone-in, skin-on chicken breasts
- 2 tablespoons honey
- 1 tablespoon sesame oil
- 1 tablespoon gluten-free tamari or soy sauce
- 1 cup chicken or vegetable broth

Directions:

Preheat the oven to 400°F.

Arrange the green beans on a large rimmed baking sheet.

Put the chicken, skin-side up, on top of the beans.

Drizzle with the honey, oil, and tamari. Add the broth.

Roast within 35 to 40 minutes. Remove, let it rest for 5 minutes and serve.

Nutrition:

- Calories: 378
- Total Fat: 10g
- Total Carbohydrates: 19g
- Sugar: 10g
- Fiber: 4g
- Protein: 54g
- Sodium: 336mg

Sheet Pan Turkey Breast with Golden Vegetables

Preparation Time: 15 minutes

Cooking Time: 45 minutes

Servings: 4

Ingredients:

- 2 tablespoons unsalted butter, at room temperature
- 1 medium acorn squash, seeded and thinly sliced
- 2 large golden beets, peeled and thinly sliced
- ½ medium yellow onion, thinly sliced
- ½ boneless, skin-on turkey breast (1 to 2 pounds)
- 2 tablespoons honey
- 1 teaspoon salt
- 1 teaspoon turmeric
- ¼ teaspoon freshly ground black pepper
- 1 cup chicken broth or vegetable broth

Directions:

Preheat the oven to 400°F. Grease the baking sheet with the butter.

Arrange the squash, beets, and onion in a single layer on the baking sheet. Put the turkey skin-side up. Drizzle with the honey. Season with the salt, turmeric, and pepper, and add the broth.

Roast until the turkey registers 165°F in the center with an instant-read thermometer, 35 to 45 minutes. Remove, and let rest for 5 minutes.

Slice, and serve.

Nutrition:

- Calories: 383
- Total Fat: 15g
- Total Carbohydrates: 25g
- Sugar: 13g
- Fiber: 3g
- Protein: 37g
- Sodium: 748mg

Sheet Pan Steak With Brussels Sprouts And Red Wine

Preparation Time: 10 minutes

Cooking Time: 20 minutes

Servings: 4

Ingredients:

- 1-pound rib-eye steak
- 1 teaspoon salt
- ¼ teaspoon freshly ground black pepper
- 1 tablespoon unsalted butter
- ½ red onion, minced
- 8 ounces Brussels sprouts, trimmed and quartered
- 1 cup red wine
- Juice of ½ lemon

Directions:

Preheat the broiler on high.

Massage the steak with the salt and pepper on a large rimmed baking sheet. Broil until browned, 2 to 3 minutes per side.

Turn off and heat-up the oven to 400°F.

Put the steak on one side of the baking sheet and add the butter, onion, Brussels sprouts, and wine to the other side.

Roast within 8 minutes. Remove, and let rest for 5 minutes.

Sprinkle with the lemon juice and serve.

Nutrition:

- Calories: 416
- Total Fat: 27g
- Total Carbohydrates: 8g
- Sugar: 2g
- Fiber: 3g

- Protein: 22g
- Sodium: 636mg

Miso Salmon and Green Beans

Preparation Time: 10 minutes

Cooking Time: 25 minutes

Servings: 4

Ingredients:

- 1 tablespoon sesame oil
- 1-pound green beans, trimmed
- 1-pound skin-on salmon fillets, cut into 4 steaks
- ¼ cup white miso
- 2 teaspoons gluten-free tamari or soy sauce
- 2 scallions, thinly sliced

Directions:

Preheat the oven to 400°F. Grease the baking sheet with the oil.

Put the green beans, then the salmon on top of the green beans, and brush each piece with the miso.

Roast within 20 to 25 minutes.

Drizzle with the tamari, sprinkle with the scallions, and serve.

Nutrition:

- Calories: 213
- Total Fat: 7g
- Total Carbohydrates: 13g
- Sugar: 3g
- Fiber: 5g
- Protein: 27g
- Sodium: 989mg

Tilapia with Asparagus And Acorn Squash

Preparation Time: 15 minutes

Cooking Time: 30 minutes

Servings: 4

Ingredients:

- 2 tablespoons extra-virgin olive oil
- 1 medium acorn squash, seeded and thinly sliced or in wedges
- 1-pound asparagus, trimmed of woody ends and cut into 2-inch pieces
- 1 large shallot, thinly sliced
- 1-pound tilapia fillets
- ½ cup white wine
- 1 tablespoon chopped fresh flat-leaf parsley
- 1 teaspoon salt
- ¼ teaspoon freshly ground black pepper

Directions:

Preheat the oven to 400°F. Grease the baking sheet with the oil.

Arrange the squash, asparagus, and shallot in a single layer on the baking sheet. Roast within 8 to 10 minutes.

Put the tilapia, and add the wine.

Sprinkle with the parsley, salt, and pepper.

Roast within 15 minutes. Remove, then let rest for 5 minutes, and serve.

Nutrition:

- Calories: 246
- Total Fat: 8g
- Total Carbohydrates: 17g
- Sugar: 2g
- Fiber: 4g
- Protein: 25g
- Sodium: 639mg

Shrimp-Lime Bake with Zucchini And Corn

Preparation Time: 10 minutes

Cooking Time: 20 minutes

Servings: 4

Ingredients:

- 1 tablespoon extra-virgin olive oil
- 2 small zucchinis, cut into ¼-inch dice
- 1 cup frozen corn kernels
- 2 scallions, thinly sliced

- 1 teaspoon salt
- ½ teaspoon ground cumin
- ½ teaspoon chipotle chili powder
- 1-pound peeled shrimp, thawed if necessary
- 1 tablespoon finely chopped fresh cilantro
- Zest and juice of 1 lime

Directions:

Preheat the oven to 400°F. Grease the baking sheet with the oil.

On the baking sheet, combine the zucchini, corn, scallions, salt, cumin, and chile powder and mix well. Arrange in a single layer.

Add the shrimp on top. Roast within 15 to 20 minutes.

Put the cilantro and lime zest and juice, stir to combine, and serve.

Nutrition:

- Calories: 184
- Total Fat: 5g
- Total Carbohydrates: 11g
- Sugar: 3g
- Fiber: 2g
- Protein: 26g
- Sodium: 846mg

Broccolini with Almonds

Preparation Time: 15 minutes

Cooking Time: 5 minutes

Servings: 6

Ingredients:

- 1 fresh red chili, deseeded and finely chopped
- 2 bunches of broccolini, trimmed
- 1 tablespoon extra-virgin olive oil
- 2 garlic cloves, thinly sliced
- 1/4 cup natural almonds, coarsely chopped
- 2 teaspoons lemon rind, finely grated
- 4 anchovies in oil, chopped
- A squeeze of fresh lemon juice

Directions:

Preheat some oil in a pan. Add 2 teaspoons of lemon rind, drained anchovies, finely chopped chili, and thinly sliced gloves. Cook for about 30 seconds, with constant stirring.

Add 1/4 cup coarsely chopped almonds and cook for a minute. Turn the heat off and add lemon juice on top.

Place the steamer basket over a pan with simmering water. Add broccolini to a basket and cover it.

Cook until tender-crisp, for about 3-4 minutes. Drain and then transfer to the serving platter.

Top with almond mixture and enjoy!

Nutrition:

- 414 calories
- 6.6 g fat
- 1.6 g total carbs
- 5.4 g protein

Tilapia with Pecan Rosemary Topping

Preparation Time: 15 minutes

Cooking Time: 18 minutes

Servings: 4

Ingredients:

- 4 tilapia fillets
- 1/3 cup raw pecans, chopped
- 1 egg white
- 1/3 cup whole-wheat panko breadcrumbs
- 1/2 teaspoon brown sugar
- 1 1/2 teaspoons olive oil
- 2 teaspoons fresh rosemary, chopped
- 1/8 teaspoon salt
- Pinch of cayenne pepper

Directions:

Add brown sugar, 1/3 cup breadcrumbs, 2 teaspoons of fresh rosemary, a pinch of cayenne pepper, 1/8 teaspoon salt, and 1/3 cup chopped pecans baking dish. Mix everything.

Drizzle with oil and toss well until coated—Preheat the oven to 350 F.

Bake the dish for about 7-8 minutes until golden brown. Increase the temperature to 400 F.

Coat the baking dish with cooking spray. Add egg whites to a shallow dish and whisk, then dip each fish fillet into the egg and then coat with pecan mixture.

Transfer coated fillets to a prepared baking dish, followed by the remaining pecan mixture.

Bake for about 10 minutes or until cooked thoroughly. Serve right away!

Nutrition:

- 222 calories
- 10.8 g fat
- 6.7 g total carbs
- 26.8 g protein

Steamed Trout with Red Bean and Chili Salsa

Preparation Time: 15 minutes

Cooking Time: 16 minutes

Servings: 1

Ingredients:

- 4 ½ oz cherry tomatoes, halved
- 1/4 avocado, unpeeled
- 6 oz skinless ocean trout fillet
- Coriander leaves to serve
- 2 teaspoons olive oil
- Lime wedges, to serve
- 4 ½ oz canned red kidney beans, rinsed and drained
- 1/2 red onion, thinly sliced
- 1 tablespoon pickled jalapenos, drained
- 1/2 teaspoon ground cumin
- 4 Sicilian olives/green olives

Directions:

Put a steamer basket over a pot of simmering water. Add fish to the basket and cover, cook for 10-12 minutes.

Remove the fish, then let it rest for a few minutes. In the meantime, preheat some oil in a pan.

Add pickled jalapenos, red kidney beans, olives, 1/2 teaspoon cumin, and cherry tomatoes. Cook for about 4-5 minutes, stirring continuously.

Scoop the bean batter onto a serving platter, followed by trout. Add coriander and onion on top.

Serve along with lime wedges and avocado. Enjoy steamed ocean trout with red bean and chili salsa!

Nutrition:

- 243 calories
- 33.2 g fat
- 18.8 g total carbs
- 44 g protein

Ratatouille

Preparation Time: 15 minutes

Cooking Time: 55 minutes

Servings: 4

Ingredients:

- 1 red onion, thickly sliced
- 5 tablespoons olive oil
- 2 tablespoons thyme leaves
- 2 garlic cloves, smashed
- 3 tomatoes, thickly sliced
- 2 sprigs oregano
- 2 red bell peppers, sides cut off and halved
- 1 cup tomato puree/tomato sauce
- 2 medium zucchinis, thickly sliced
- 1 small eggplant, thickly sliced
- 2 medium summer squash, thickly sliced
- Salt, to taste
- Freshly ground black pepper, to taste

Directions:

Preheat the oven to 375 F.

Place a baking dish on a baking sheet. Preheat some olive oil in a small pot over medium heat. Cook garlic for a minute, until fragrant.

Turn off the heat, and put 2 sprigs of oregano. Let it rest for about 15-20 minutes.

Now discard both oregano and garlic—Grease the baking dish with 2 tablespoons of oil.

Add 4 tablespoons of tomato puree to the baking dish and spread evenly. Now add a layer of zucchini, eggplant, tomato, onion, and summer squash. Repeat the layer.

Brush the top with leftover tomato puree. Drizzle with oil and sprinkle with pepper, salt, and thyme.

Bake for about 25-30 minutes, or until tender. Cool for about 5-10 minutes. Serve right away!

Nutrition:

- 283 calories
- 18 g fat
- 30 g total carbs
- 6 g protein

Italian Stuffed Peppers

Preparation Time: 15 minutes

Cooking Time: 40 minutes

Servings: 6

Ingredients:

- 1 teaspoon garlic powder
- 1/2 cup mozzarella, shredded
- 1 lb. lean ground meat
- 1/2 cup parmesan cheese
- 3 bell peppers, cut into half lengthwise, stems, seeds and ribs removed
- 1 (10 oz.) package frozen spinach
- 2 cups marinara sauce
- 1/2 teaspoon salt
- 1 teaspoon Italian seasoning

Directions:

Coat a foil-lined baking sheet with non-stick spray. Place the peppers on the baking pan.

Add turkey to a non-stick pan and cook over medium heat until no longer pink.

When almost cooked, add 2 cups of marinara sauce and seasonings—Cook for about 8-10 minutes.

Add spinach along with 1/2 cup parmesan cheese. Stir until well-combined.

Add half cup of the meat mixture into each pepper and divide cheese among all—Preheat the oven to 450 F.

Bake peppers for about 25-30 minutes. Cool, and serve.

Nutrition:

- 150 calories
- 2 g fat
- 11 g total carbs
- 20 g protein

Lemon Herb Salmon and Zucchini

Preparation Time: 15 minutes

Cooking Time: 20 minutes

Servings: 4

Ingredients:

- 4 zucchinis, chopped
- 2 tablespoons olive oil
- Salt, to taste
- Freshly ground black pepper, to taste

For the Salmon:

- 4 salmon fillets
- 1/2 teaspoon dried oregano
- 2 tablespoons fresh parsley leaves, chopped
- 2 tablespoons brown sugar, packed
- 2 tablespoons freshly squeezed lemon juice
- Kosher salt, to taste
- Freshly ground black pepper, to taste
- 1 tablespoon Dijon mustard
- 1/4 teaspoon dried rosemary
- 2 garlic cloves, minced
- 1/4 teaspoon dried thyme
- 1/2 teaspoon dried dill

Directions:

Coat the baking sheet with nonstick spray. Preheat the oven to 400 F.

Add garlic, 1/2 teaspoon dried dill, 1 tablespoon Dijon mustard, 1/2 teaspoon dried oregano, 2 tablespoons brown sugar, lemon juice, 2 pinches of thyme, and rosemary to a bowl. Whisk well and season with pepper and salt to taste. Keep it aside.

Spread zucchini onto a coated baking sheet. Drizzle with oil and sprinkle with pepper and salt. Now arrange salmon evenly on top and brush with herb mixture.

Bake within 18 minutes. Garnish lemon herb salmon and zucchini with parsley and serve right away!

Nutrition:

- 330 calories
- 16.7 g fat
- 14.7 g total carbs
- 31 g protein

Sweet Potato Black Bean Burgers

Preparation Time: 15 minutes

Cooking Time: 10 minutes

Servings: 6

Ingredients:

- 1/2 jalapeno, seeded and diced
- 1/2 cup quinoa
- 6 whole-grain hamburger buns
- 1 can black beans, rinsed and drained
- Olive oil/coconut oil, for cooking
- 1 sweet potato
- 1/2 cup red onion, diced
- 4 tablespoons gluten-free oat flour
- 2 cloves garlic, minced
- 2 teaspoons spicy cajun seasoning
- 1/2 cup cilantro, chopped
- 1 teaspoon cumin
- Sprouts
- Salt, to taste
- Pepper, to taste

For the Crema:

- 2 tablespoons cilantro, chopped
- 1/2 ripe avocado, diced
- 4 tablespoons low-fat sour cream/plain Greek yogurt
- 1 teaspoon lime juice

Directions:

Rinse quinoa under cold running water. Put a cup of water in a saucepan and heat it. Add quinoa and bring to a boil.

Cover, then simmer over low heat until all of the water has absorbed, for about 15 minutes.

Turn the heat off and fluff quinoa with a fork. Then transfer quinoa to a bowl and let it cool for 5-10 minutes.

Poke potato with a fork and then microwave for a few minutes, until thoroughly cooked and soft. Once cooked, peel the potato and let it cool.

Add cooked potato to a food processor along with 1 can black beans, ½ cup chopped cilantro, 2 teaspoons of Cajun seasoning, ½ cup diced onion, 1 teaspoon cumin, and 2 minced cloves of garlic. Pulse until you obtain a smooth mixture. Transfer it to a bowl and add cooked quinoa.

Add in oat flour/oat bran. Mix well and shape into 6 patties. Put patties on a baking sheet and refrigerate for about half an hour.

Add all the Crema ingredients to a food processor. Pulse until smooth. Adjust salt to taste and refrigerate.

Grease a cooking pan with oil and heat it over medium heat. Cook each side of patties until light golden, just for 3-4 minutes. Serve with crema, sprouts, buns, and along with any of your favorite toppings.

Nutrition:

- 206 calories
- 6 g fat
- 33.9 g total carbs
- 7.9 g protein

Turkey and Quinoa Stuffed Peppers

Preparation Time: 15 minutes

Cooking Time: 45 minutes

Servings: 4

Ingredients:

- 1 cup fresh spinach, chopped
- 1 cup quinoa, cooked
- 3 large yellow peppers, stems and seeds removed, cut into half

- 1 cup chicken broth
- 1.25 lb. extra lean ground turkey
- 1 cup (18 oz. can) tomato sauce
- 1 cup mushrooms, diced
- 2 teaspoons garlic, minced
- 1/4 cup sweet onion, diced

Directions:

Preheat some oil in a pan and add vegetables. Sauté for about 5 minutes and then add 2 teaspoons of minced garlic along with the ground turkey. Cook until meat is thoroughly cooked. Add in 1 cup chicken broth and 1 cup tomato sauce. Simmer over low heat.

In the meantime, spray your baking pan with cooking spray. Arrange bell peppers into the pan.

When the quinoa is cooked, put it into the pan with veggies and turkey. Stir until well-combined.

Now stuff the bell peppers with the mixture. Pour remaining chicken broth into the baking pan around peppers—Preheat the oven to 400 F.

Cover the pan with foil—Cook for about 30-35 minutes. Serve and enjoy!

Nutrition:

- 640 calories
- 13 g fat
- 74 g total carbs
- 53 g protein

Avocado Pesto Zoodles with Salmon

Preparation Time: 15 minutes

Cooking Time: 25 minutes

Servings: 4

Ingredients:

- 1 tablespoon pesto
- 1 lemon
- 2 frozen/fresh salmon steaks
- 1 large zucchini, spiralized
- 1 tablespoon black pepper
- 1 avocado
- 1/4 cup parmesan, grated
- Italian seasoning

Directions:

Heat-up the oven to 375 F. Season salmon with Italian seasoning, salt, and pepper and bake for 20 minutes.

Add avocados to the bowl along with a tablespoon of pepper, lemon juice, and a tablespoon of pesto Mash the avocados and keep it aside.

Add zucchini noodles to a serving platter, followed by avocado mixture and salmon.

Sprinkle with cheese. Add more pesto if needed. Enjoy!

Nutrition:

- 128 calories
- 9.9 g fat
- 9 g total carbs
- 4 g protein

Salmon Cakes

Preparation Time: 15 minutes

Cooking Time: 15 minutes

Servings: 4

Ingredients:

- 1/2 lemon, zested
- 6 tablespoons vegetable oil
- 2 strips rasher bacon, cooked and crumbled, bacon fat reserved
- 2 oz onion, chopped
- 2 tablespoons Parmesan, grated
- 1 egg
- 1 ½ tablespoons breadcrumbs
- ½ cup mayonnaise
- 1 baked or boiled potato, peeled and fluffed with a fork
- 2 teaspoon Dijon mustard
- 1 tin (14 oz) wild salmon
- 1/2 teaspoon granulated sugar
- Freshly ground black pepper, to taste

Directions:

Preheat reserved bacon fat (about 1 tablespoon) in a pan over medium heat. Put the chopped onions and cook for a few minutes until translucent. Let the onions cool for 10 minutes.

In a bowl, mix mayonnaise, Dijon mustard, lemon zest, cooked onions, bacon, 1/2 teaspoon sugar, and 1 egg. Mix well and then add potato along with salmon. Shape the mixture into about 12 patties.

Mix 2 tablespoons of grated parmesan, pepper, and breadcrumbs in a separate bowl. Coat the patties in this mixture one by one.

Put 3 tablespoons of oil to a pan and heat it. Add salmon cakes and cook in batches. Cook both sides within 3-4 minutes until golden. Add more oil if needed.

Transfer to a serving platter and enjoy!

Nutrition:

- 395 calories
- 32.7 g fat
- 19 g total carbs
- 7 g protein

Chicken and Snap Pea Stir-Fry

Preparation Time: 15 minutes

Cooking Time: 10 minutes

Servings: 4

Ingredients:

- 1 ¼ cups boneless skinless chicken breast, thinly sliced
- 3 tablespoons fresh cilantro, chopped
- 2 tablespoons vegetable oil
- 2 tablespoons of sesame seeds
- 1 bunch scallions, thinly sliced
- 2 teaspoons Sriracha
- 2 garlic cloves, minced
- 2 tablespoons rice vinegar
- 1 bell pepper, thinly sliced
- 3 tablespoons soy sauce
- 2½ cups snap peas
- Salt, to taste
- Freshly ground black pepper, to taste

Directions:

Heat-up the oil in a pan over medium heat. Add garlic and thinly sliced scallions. Cook for a minute and then add 2 ½ cups snap peas along with bell pepper. Cook until tender, just for about 3-4 minutes.

Add chicken and cook for about 4-5 minutes, or until thoroughly cooked.

Add in 2 teaspoons Sriracha, 2 tablespoons of sesame seeds, 3 tablespoons soy sauce, and 2 tablespoons rice vinegar. Toss everything until well-combined. Simmer within 2-3 minutes over low heat.

Add 3 tablespoons of chopped cilantro and stir well. Transfer, and sprinkle with extra sesame seeds and cilantro, if needed. Enjoy!

Nutrition:

- 228 calories
- 11 g fat
- 11 g total carbs
- 20 g protein

Balsamic Chicken

Preparation Time: 15 minutes

Cooking Time: 15 minutes

Servings: 4

Ingredients:

- 1/2 cup roasted pumpkin seeds
- 3 tablespoons olive oil
- 1/2 cup dried cranberries
- 15-20 Brussels sprouts, trimmed and halved into lengthwise
- 1/2 cup sun-dried tomatoes, not oil-packed
- 1 1/4 lbs. boneless chicken breast, cut into bite-sized pieces
- 2 tablespoons honey
- 1 shallot, peeled and diced
- 4 tablespoons balsamic vinegar
- Salt, to taste
- Pepper, to taste

Directions:

Preheat 2 tablespoons of oil in a skillet over medium heat. Add Brussels sprouts cut side down.

Cook until seared for about 4-5 minutes. Flip Brussels sprouts and move them aside.

Add more oil to the pan. Add diced shallots and chicken. Put the pepper and salt to taste and cook until chicken is thoroughly cooked, for about 4-5 minutes. Stir and flip the chicken.

Drizzle with honey and balsamic vinegar, stir. Simmer for few minutes.

Arrange 1/2 cup dried cranberries, 1/2 cup sun-dried tomatoes, and 1/2 cup pumpkin seeds evenly over the top. Stir until combined.

Serve immediately and enjoy!

Nutrition:

- 534 calories
- 31 g fat
- 29 g total carbs
- 34 g protein

Pineapple Fried Rice

Preparation Time: 15 minutes

Cooking Time: 20 minutes

Servings: 4

Ingredients:

- 2 carrots, peeled and grated
- 2 green onions, sliced
- 3 tablespoons soy sauce
- 1/2 cup ham, diced
- 1 tablespoon sesame oil
- 2 cups canned/fresh pineapple, diced
- 1/2 teaspoon ginger powder
- 3 cups brown rice, cooked
- 1/4 teaspoon white pepper
- 2 tablespoons olive oil
- 1/2 cup frozen peas
- 2 garlic cloves, minced
- 1/2 cup frozen corn
- 1 onion, diced

Directions:

Put 1 tablespoon sesame oil, 3 tablespoons soy sauce, 2 pinches of white pepper, and 1/2 teaspoon ginger powder in a bowl. Mix well and keep it aside.

Preheat oil in a skillet. Add the garlic along with the diced onion. Cook for about 3-4 minutes, stirring often.

Add 1/2 cup frozen peas, grated carrots, and 1/2 cup frozen corn. Stir until veggies are tender, just for few minutes.

Stir in soy sauce mixture, 2 cups of diced pineapple, ½ cup chopped ham, 3 cups cooked brown rice, and sliced green onions. Cook for about 2-3 minutes, stirring often. Serve!

Nutrition:

- 252 calories
- 12.8 g fat
- 33 g total carbs
- 3 g protein

Chicken Roast with Turmeric and Fennel

Preparation Time: 15 minutes

Cooking Time: 45 minutes

Servings: 6

Ingredients:

- 3/4 tablespoon ground turmeric spice
- 1 lime, thinly sliced
- 1/2 cup extra virgin olive oil
- 2 oranges, unpeeled and sliced
- 1/2 cup dry white wine
- 6 pieces bone-in, skin-on chicken
- 1/2 cup orange juice
- 1 large sweet onion
- 1 lime, juiced
- 1 fennel bulb, cored and sliced
- 2 tablespoons yellow mustard
- 3 tablespoons brown sugar
- 1 teaspoon sweet paprika
- 1 tablespoon garlic powder
- 1 teaspoon ground coriander
- Salt, to taste

- Pepper, to taste

Directions:

Preheat the oven to 475 F.

Mix lime juice, 1/2 cup olive oil, 1/2 cup orange juice, 1/2 cup dry white wine, 3 tablespoons brown sugar, and 2 tablespoons yellow mustard in a bowl.

Take another bowl and add 1 tablespoon garlic powder, 1 teaspoon ground coriander, pepper, salt, 3/4 tablespoon turmeric spice, and 1 teaspoon sweet paprika—transfer half of this spice mixture to the prepared marinade. Mix well until combined.

Pat dry chicken pieces, then season with the leftover spice mix. Add this chicken to the bowl with marinade along with leftover ingredients. Mix.

Cover, and chill for about 1-2 hours—transfer chicken to the baking pan along with the marinade, then roast for 40-45 minutes. Serve right away!

Nutrition:

- 559 calories
- 36.3 g fat
- 26 g total carbs
- 34 g protein

Roasted Salmon with Potatoes and Romaine

Preparation Time: 15 minutes

Cooking Time: 30 minutes

Servings: 4

Ingredients:

- 2 hearts romaine lettuce, cut into half
- 1 lb. baby Yukon Gold potatoes
- ¼ teaspoon paprika
- ¼ cup olive oil, divided
- 1 tablespoon butter, melted
- 1 teaspoon lemon juice
- 4 salmon fillets
- Salt, to taste
- Freshly ground black pepper, to taste

Directions:

Add potatoes to a bowl and toss with 2 tablespoons of oil. Arrange these potatoes onto a greased baking sheet. Preheat the oven to 400 F.

Roast within 15-20 minutes, until fork-tender and golden.

Coat the romaine hearts with lemon juice and 2 tablespoons of oil. Sprinkle with pepper and salt, to taste. Keep aside.

Brush melted butter all over the salmon. Sprinkle each fillet with paprika, pepper, and salt.

Arrange salmon and romaine with potatoes on a baking sheet. Roast within 7-8 minutes.

Transfer to a serving platter and enjoy!

Nutrition:

- 611 calories
- 40 g fat
- 25 g total carbs
- 39 g protein

Quinoa Salad

Preparation Time: 10 Minutes

Cooking Time: 40 Minutes

Servings: 4 to 6

Ingredients:

- ½ cup Lemon juice, fresh
- 2 cups Quinoa, dry
- 1 Red Pepper, large & roasted
- 1 cup Scallions, finely minced
- 1 cup Dill, fresh & chopped
- ½ of 1 Red Onion, finely chopped
- 13 Olives, chopped
- 1 Cucumber, chopped
- 4 cups Water
- 1 cup Parsley, fresh & chopped
- ¼ cup Extra Virgin Olive Oil
- 2 tsp. Sea Salt

Directions:

Begin by cooking the quinoa in 4 cups of water in a medium-sized deep saucepan over medium heat.

Now, bring the quinoa mixture to a boil, and once it starts boiling, lower the heat.

Cook it for another 13 to 15 minutes or until the quinoa absorbs all the water. Fluff the quinoa by using a fork.

In the meantime, mix olive oil, black pepper, lime juice, and sea salt in a large-sized mixing bowl until combined well.

Then, spoon in the cooked quinoa and toss them well.

Finally, add the scallions, parsley, dill, olives, red peppers, and cucumber to the bowl.

Toss well until the dressing coats all the chopped vegetables.

Chill the salad for a minimum of one hour before serving.

Nutrition:

- Calories: 325Kcal
- Proteins:4.4g
- Carbohydrates: 34.3g
- Fat: 5.1g

Broccoli Tuna

Preparation Time: 5 Minutes

Cooking Time: 10 Minutes

Servings: 1

Ingredients:

- 1 tsp. Extra Virgin Olive Oil
- 3oz. Tuna in water, preferably light & chunky, drained
- 1 tbsp. Walnuts, chopped coarsely
- 2 cups Broccoli, chopped finely
- ½ tsp. Hot Sauce

Directions:

Begin by mixing broccoli, seasoning & tuna in a large-sized mixing bowl until they are well combined.

Then, microwave the veggies in the oven for 3 minutes or until tender

Then, stir in the walnuts and olive oil to the bowl and mix well.

Serve and enjoy.

Nutrition:

- Calories: 259Kcal
- Proteins:27.1g
- Carbohydrates: 12.9g
- Fat: 12.4g

Cauliflower Rice

Preparation Time: 25 Minutes

Cooking Time: 10 Minutes

Servings: 4

Ingredients:

- ¼ cup Cooking Oil
- 1 tbsp. Coconut Oil
- 1 tbsp. Coconut Sugar
- 4 cups Cauliflower, broken down into florets
- ½ tsp. Salt

Directions:

First, process the cauliflower in a food processor and process it for 1 to 2 minutes.

Heat-up the oil in a large skillet over medium heat, then spoon in the riced cauliflower, coconut sugar, and salt to the pan.

Combine them well and cook them for 4 to 5 minutes or until the cauliflower is slightly soft.

Finally, pour the coconut milk and enjoy it.

Nutrition:

- Calories: 108Kcal
- Proteins:27.1g
- Carbohydrates: 11g
- Fat: 6g

Orange Chicken Salad

Preparation Time: 10 Minutes

Cooking Time: 25 Minutes

Servings: 2

Ingredients:

- 5 oz. Spinach
- 4 Navel Oranges, large
- 1 Red Onion, small & halved & sliced

- ¼ cup Olive Oil
- 4 × 6 oz. Chicken Breast, boneless & skinless
- 1 tbsp. Honey
- ½ tsp. Black Pepper
- 2 tbsp. Apple Cider Vinegar
- ½ tsp. Salt

Directions:

First, squeeze out orange juice from 2 oranges and then mix it with 3 tbsp of olive oil, pepper, vinegar, honey, and pepper in a small-sized bowl until combined well.

After that, spoon out 5 tbsp of this orange juice mixture to another zip lock bag and then place the chicken pieces. Marinate the chicken for 15 minutes or a maximum period of 2 hours.

Slice the remaining orange into segments and place them in a medium-sized bowl.

Heat a grill pan over medium-high heat.

To this, stir in the grilled chicken and cook for 5 minutes per side or until cooked entirely.

Then, spoon in oil in another large skillet over medium heat.

Once the oil becomes hot, add the onion and sauté them for 1 to 2 minutes or until softened.

Spoon in the remaining juice to this and sauté for 1 minute.

Remove, and add the orange segments. To serve, place the spinach first on the palate, followed by half of the orange mixture. Top with the grilled chicken. Spoon the orange juice mixture over it.

Nutrition:

- Calories: 669Kcal
- Proteins:97.8g
- Carbohydrates: 19.6g
- Fat: 20g

Vegetable Soup

Preparation Time: 10 Minutes

Cooking Time: 40 Minutes

Servings: 4

Ingredients:

- 1 tbsp. Coconut Oil
- 2 cups Kale, chopped
- 2 Celery Stalks, diced
- ½ of 15 oz. can of White Beans, drained & rinsed
- 1 Onion, large & diced
- ¼ tsp. Black Pepper
- 1 Carrot, medium & diced
- 2 cups Cauliflower, cut into florets
- 1 tsp. Turmeric, grounded
- 1 tsp. Sea Salt
- 3 Garlic cloves, minced
- 6 cups Vegetable Broth

Directions:

To start with, heat oil in a large pot over medium-low heat.

Stir in the onion to the pot and sauté it for 5 minutes or until softened.

Put the carrot plus celery to the pot and continue cooking for another 4 minutes or until the veggies softened.

Now, spoon in the turmeric, garlic, and ginger to the mixture. Stir well.

Cook the veggie mixture for 1 minute or until fragrant.

Then, pour the vegetable broth along with salt and pepper and bring the mixture to a boil.

Once it starts boiling, add the cauliflower. Reduce the heat and simmer the vegetable mixture for 13 to 15 minutes or until the cauliflower is softened.

Finally, add the beans and kale—Cook within 2 minutes.

Serve it hot.

Nutrition:

- Calories: 192Kcal
- Proteins:12.6g
- Carbohydrates: 24.6g
- Fat: 6.4g

Beets Gazpacho

Preparation Time: 10 Minutes

Cooking Time: 10 Minutes

Servings: 4

Ingredients:

- 1× 20oz. Can Great Northern Beans, rinsed and drained
- ¼ tsp. Kosher Salt
- 1 tbsp. Extra-Virgin Olive Oil
- ½ tsp. Garlic, fresh and minced
- 1× 6oz. pouch Pink Salmon flaked
- 2 tbsp. Lemon juice, freshly squeezed
- 4 Green Onions, sliced thinly
- ½ tsp. Ground Black Pepper
- ½ tsp. Lemon rind grated
- ¼ cup Flat-leaf Parsley, fresh and chopped

Directions:

First, place lemon rind, olive oil, lemon juice, black pepper, and garlic in a medium-sized mixing bowl and mix them with a whisker.

Combine beans, onions, salmon, and parsley in another medium-sized bowl and toss them well.

Then, spoon in the lemon juice dressing over the bean's mixture. Mix well ` until the dressing coats the beans mixture.

Serve and enjoy.

Nutrition:

- Calories: 131Kcal
- Proteins:1.9g
- Carbohydrates: 14.8g
- Fat: 8.5g

Lentil Curry

Preparation Time: 10 Minutes

Cooking Time: 40 Minutes

Servings: 4

Ingredients:

- 2 tsp. Mustard Seeds
- 1 tsp. Turmeric, grounded
- 1 cup Lentils, soaked
- 2 tsp. Cumin Seeds
- 1 Tomato, large & chopped
- 1 Yellow Onion, sliced finely
- 4 cups Water
- Sea Salt, as needed
- 2 Carrots, sliced into half-moons
- 3 handful of Spinach leaves, shredded
- 1 tsp. Ginger, minced
- ½ tsp. Chili Powder
- 2 tbsp. Coconut Oil

Directions:

First, place the mung beans and water in a deep saucepan over medium-high heat.

Now, bring the beans mixture to a boil and allow it to simmer.

Simmer within 20 to 30 minutes or until the mung beans are softened.

Then, heat the coconut oil in a large saucepan over medium heat and stir in the mustard seeds and cumin seeds.

If the mustard seeds pop, put the onions. Sauté the onions for 4 minutes or until they softened.

Spoon in the garlic and continue sautéing for another 1 minute. Once aromatic, spoon in the turmeric and chili powder to it.

Then, add the carrot and tomato—Cook for 6 minutes or until softened.

Finally, add the cooked lentils to it and give everything a good stir.

Stir in the spinach leaves and sauté until wilted. Remove from heat. Serve it warm and enjoy.

Nutrition:

- Calories: 290Kcal
- Proteins: 14g
- Carbohydrates: 43g
- Fat: 8g

Creamy Turmeric Cauliflower Soup

Preparation Time: 10 minutes

Cooking Time: 15 minutes

Servings: 4

Ingredients:

- 2 tablespoons extra-virgin olive oil
- 1 leek, white part only, thinly sliced
- 3 cups cauliflower florets
- 1 garlic clove, peeled
- 1 (1¼-inch) piece fresh ginger, peeled and sliced
- 1½ teaspoons turmeric
- ½ teaspoon salt
- ¼ teaspoon freshly ground black pepper
- ¼ teaspoon ground cumin
- 3 cups vegetable broth
- 1 cup full-Fat: coconut milk
- ¼ cup finely chopped fresh cilantro

Directions:

Heat-up the oil over high heat in a large pot.

Sauté the leek within 3 to 4 minutes.

Put the cauliflower, garlic, ginger, turmeric, salt, pepper, and cumin and sauté for 1 to 2 minutes.

Put the broth, and boil.

Simmer within 5 minutes.

Purée the soup using an immersion blender until smooth.

Stir in the coconut milk and cilantro, heat through, and serve.

Nutrition:

- Calories: 264
- Total Fat: 23g
- Total Carbohydrates: 12g
- Sugar: 5g
- Fiber: 4g
- Protein: 7g
- Sodium: 900mg

"Eat Your Greens" Soup

Preparation Time: 10 minutes

Cooking Time: 20 minutes

Servings: 4

Ingredients:

- ¼ cup extra-virgin olive oil
- 2 leeks, white parts only, thinly sliced
- 1 fennel bulb, trimmed and thinly sliced
- 1 garlic clove, peeled
- 1 bunch Swiss chard, coarsely chopped
- 4 cups coarsely chopped kale
- 4 cups coarsely chopped mustard greens
- 3 cups vegetable broth
- 2 tablespoons apple cider vinegar
- 1 teaspoon salt
- ¼ teaspoon freshly ground black pepper
- ¼ cup chopped cashews (optional)

Directions:

Heat-up the oil over high heat in a large pot.

Add the leeks, fennel, and garlic and sauté until softened, for about 5 minutes.

Add the Swiss chard, kale, and mustard greens and sauté until the greens wilt, 2 to 3 minutes.

Put the broth and boil.

Simmer within 5 minutes.

Stir in the vinegar, salt, pepper, and cashews (if using).

Purée the soup using an immersion blender until smooth and serve.

Nutrition:

- Calories: 238
- Total Fat: 14g
- Total Carbohydrates: 22g
- Sugar: 4g
- Fiber: 6g
- Protein: 9g
- Sodium: 1294mg

Sweet Potato and Corn Soup

Preparation Time: 10 minutes

Cooking Time: 20 minutes

Servings: 4

Ingredients:

- ¼ cup extra-virgin olive oil or coconut oil
- 1 medium zucchini, cut into ¼-inch dice
- 1 cup broccoli florets
- 1 cup thinly sliced mushrooms
- 1 small onion, cut into ¼-inch dice
- 4 cups vegetable broth
- 2 cups peeled sweet potatoes cut into ¼-inch dice
- 1 cup frozen corn kernels
- 1 cup coconut milk or almond milk
- 2 tablespoons finely chopped fresh flat-leaf parsley
- 1 teaspoon salt
- ¼ teaspoon freshly ground black pepper

Directions:

Heat-up the oil over high heat.

Add the zucchini, broccoli, mushrooms, and onion and sauté until softened, 5 to 8 minutes.

Put the broth and sweet potatoes, boil.

Simmer within 5 to 7 minutes.

Add the corn, coconut milk, parsley, salt, and pepper. Cook on low heat and serve.

Nutrition:

- Calories: 402
- Total Fat: 29g
- Total Carbohydrates: 31g
- Sugar: 9g
- Fiber: 6g
- Protein: 10g
- Sodium: 1406mg

Chickpea Curry Soup

Preparation Time: 10 minutes

Cooking Time: 25 minutes

Servings: 4

Ingredients:

- ¼ cup extra-virgin olive oil or coconut oil
- 1 medium onion, finely chopped
- 2 garlic cloves, sliced
- 1 large Granny Smith apple, cut into ¼-inch dice
- 2 teaspoons curry powder
- 1 teaspoon salt
- 3 cups peeled butternut squash cut into ½-inch dice
- 3 cups vegetable broth
- 1 cup full-Fat: coconut milk
- 1 (15-ounce) can chickpeas, drained and rinsed
- 2 tablespoons cilantro, chopped

Directions:

Heat-up the oil over high heat in a large pot.

Put the onion and garlic and sauté until the onion begins to brown, 6 to 8 minutes.

Put the apple, curry powder, and salt, then sauté to toast the curry powder, 1 to 2 minutes.

Add the squash and broth and boil.

Simmer within 10 minutes. Stir in the coconut milk.

Purée the soup using an immersion blender until smooth.

Stir in the chickpeas and cilantro, heat through for 1 to 2 minutes, and serve.

Nutrition:

- Calories: 469
- Total Fat: 30g
- Total Carbohydrates: 45g
- Sugar: 14g
- Fiber: 10g
- Protein: 12g
- Sodium: 1174mg

Brown Rice and Shitake Miso Soup with Scallions

Preparation Time: 10 minutes

Cooking Time: 45 minutes

Servings: 4

Ingredients:

- 2 tablespoons sesame oil
- 1 cup thinly sliced shiitake mushroom caps
- 1 garlic clove, minced
- 1 (1½-inch) piece fresh ginger, peeled and sliced
- 1 cup medium-grain brown rice
- ½ teaspoon salt
- 1 tablespoon white miso
- 2 scallions, thinly sliced
- 2 tablespoons finely chopped fresh cilantro

Directions:

Heat-up the oil over medium-high heat in a large pot.

Add the mushrooms, garlic, and ginger and sauté until the mushrooms begin to soften about 5 minutes.

Put the rice and stir to coat with the oil evenly. Add 2 cups of water and salt and boil.

Simmer within 30 to 40 minutes. Use a little of the soup broth to soften the miso, then stir it into the pot until well blended.

Mix in the scallions plus cilantro, then serve.

Nutrition:

- Calories: 265
- Total Fat: 8g
- Total Carbohydrates: 43g
- Sugar: 2g
- Fiber: 3g
- Protein: 5g
- Sodium: 456mg

Garlic and Lentil Soup

Preparation Time: 15 minutes

Cooking Time: 15 minutes

Servings: 4

Ingredients:

- 2 tablespoons extra-virgin olive oil
- 2 medium carrots, thinly sliced
- 1 small white onion, cut into ¼-inch dice
- 2 garlic cloves, thinly sliced
- 1 teaspoon ground cinnamon
- 1 teaspoon salt
- ¼ teaspoon freshly ground black pepper
- 3 cups vegetable broth
- 1 (15-ounce) can lentils, drained and rinsed
- 1 tablespoon minced or grated orange zest
- ¼ cup chopped walnuts (optional)
- 2 tablespoons finely chopped fresh flat-leaf parsley

Directions:

Heat-up the oil over high heat in a large pot.

Put the carrots, onion, and garlic and sauté until softened, 5 to 7 minutes.

Put the cinnamon, salt, and pepper and stir to coat the vegetables, 1 to 2 minutes evenly.

Put the broth and boil. Simmer, then put the lentils, and cook until within 1 minute.

Stir in the orange zest and serve, sprinkled with the walnuts (if using) and parsley.

Nutrition:

- Calories: 201
- Total Fat: 8g
- Total Carbohydrates: 22g
- Sugar: 4g
- Fiber: 8g
- Protein: 11g
- Sodium: 1178mg

Italian Summer Squash Soup

Preparation Time: 10 minutes

Cooking Time: 15 minutes

Servings: 4

Ingredients:

- 3 tablespoons extra-virgin olive oil
- 1 small red onion, thinly sliced
- 1 garlic clove, minced
- 1 cup shredded zucchini
- 1 cup shredded yellow squash
- ½ cup shredded carrot
- 3 cups vegetable broth
- 1 teaspoon salt
- 2 tablespoons finely chopped fresh basil
- 1 tablespoon finely chopped fresh chives
- 2 tablespoons pine nuts

Directions:

Heat-up the oil over high heat in a large pot.

Put the onion and garlic and sauté until softened, 5 to 7 minutes.

Add the zucchini, yellow squash, and carrot and sauté until softened, 1 to 2 minutes.

Add the broth and salt, and boil. Simmer within 1 to 2 minutes.

Stir in the basil and chives and serve, sprinkled with the pine nuts.

Nutrition:

- Calories: 172
- Total Fat: 15g
- Total Carbohydrates: 6g
- Sugar: 3g
- Fiber: 2g
- Protein: 5g
- Sodium: 1170mg

Chicken and Gluten-Free Noodle Soup

Preparation Time: 10 minutes

Cooking Time: 25 minutes

Servings: 4

Ingredients:

- ¼ cup extra-virgin olive oil
- 3 celery stalks, cut into ¼-inch slices
- 2 medium carrots, cut into ¼-inch dice
- 1 small onion, cut into ¼-inch dice
- 1 fresh rosemary sprig
- 4 cups chicken broth
- 8 ounces gluten-free penne
- 1 teaspoon salt
- ¼ teaspoon freshly ground black pepper
- 2 cups diced rotisserie chicken
- ¼ cup finely chopped fresh flat-leaf parsley

Directions:

Heat-up the oil over high heat in a large pot.

Put the celery, carrots, onion, and rosemary and sauté until softened, 5 to 7 minutes.

Add the broth, penne, salt, and pepper and boil.

Simmer and cook until the penne is tender, 8 to 10 minutes.

Remove and discard the rosemary sprig, and add the chicken and parsley.

Reduce the heat to low. Cook within 5 minutes, and serve.

Nutrition:

- Calories: 485
- Total Fat: 18g
- Total Carbohydrates: 47g
- Sugar: 4g
- Fiber: 7g
- Protein: 33g
- Sodium: 1423mg

Leek, Chicken, and Spinach Soup

Preparation Time: 10 minutes

Cooking Time: 15 minutes

Servings: 4

Ingredients:

- 3 tablespoons unsalted butter
- 2 leeks, white parts only, thinly sliced
- 4 cups baby spinach
- 4 cups chicken broth
- 1 teaspoon salt

- ¼ teaspoon freshly ground black pepper
- 2 cups shredded rotisserie chicken
- 1 tablespoon thinly sliced fresh chives
- 2 teaspoons grated or minced lemon zest

Directions:

Dissolve the butter over high heat in a large pot.

Add the leeks and sauté until softened and beginning to brown, 3 to 5 minutes.

Add the spinach, broth, salt, and pepper and boil.

Simmer within 1 to 2 minutes.

Put the chicken and cook within 1 to 2 minutes.

Sprinkle with the chives and lemon zest and serve.

Nutrition:

- Calories: 256
- Total Fat: 12g
- Total Carbohydrates: 9g
- Sugar: 3g
- Fiber: 2g
- Protein: 27g
- Sodium: 1483mg

Saffron and Salmon Soup

Preparation Time: 10 minutes

Cooking Time: 20 minutes

Servings: 4

Ingredients:

- ¼ cup extra-virgin olive oil
- 2 leeks, white parts only, thinly sliced
- 2 medium carrots, thinly sliced
- 2 garlic cloves, thinly sliced
- 4 cups vegetable broth
- 1-pound skinless salmon fillets, cut into 1-inch pieces
- 1 teaspoon salt
- ¼ teaspoon freshly ground black pepper
- ¼ teaspoon saffron threads
- 2 cups baby spinach
- ½ cup dry white wine
- 2 tablespoons chopped scallions, both white and green parts
- 2 tablespoons finely chopped fresh flat-leaf parsley

Directions:

Heat the oil over high in a large pot.

Add the leeks, carrots, and garlic and sauté until softened, 5 to 7 minutes.

Put the broth and boil.

Simmer and add the salmon, salt, pepper, and saffron. Cook until the salmon is cooked through, about 8 minutes.

Add the spinach, wine, scallions, and parsley and cook until the spinach has wilted, 1 to 2 minutes, and serve.

Nutrition:

- Calories: 418
- Total Fat: 26g
- Total Carbohydrates: 13g
- Sugar: 4g
- Fiber: 2g
- Protein: 29g
- Sodium: 1455mg

Butternut Squash Soup with Shrimp

Preparation Time: 10 minutes

Cooking Time: 20 minutes

Servings: 4

Ingredients:

- 3 tablespoons unsalted butter
- 1 small red onion, finely chopped
- 1 garlic clove, sliced
- 1 teaspoon turmeric
- 1 teaspoon salt
- ¼ teaspoon freshly ground black pepper
- 3 cups vegetable broth
- 2 cups peeled butternut squash cut into ¼-inch dice
- 1-pound cooked peeled shrimp, thawed if necessary

- 1 cup unsweetened almond milk
- ¼ cup slivered almonds (optional)
- 2 tablespoons finely chopped fresh flat-leaf parsley
- 2 teaspoons grated or minced lemon zest

Directions:

Dissolve the butter over high heat in a large pot.

Add the onion, garlic, turmeric, salt, and pepper and sauté until the vegetables are soft and translucent, 5 to 7 minutes.

Add the broth and squash and boil.

Simmer within 5 minutes.

Add the shrimp and almond milk and cook until heated through about 2 minutes.

Sprinkle with the almonds (if using), parsley, and lemon zest and serve.

Nutrition:

- Calories: 275
- Total Fat: 12g
- Total Carbohydrates: 12g
- Sugar: 3g
- Fiber: 2g
- Protein: 30g
- Sodium: 1665mg

Clear Clam Chowder

Preparation Time: 10 minutes

Cooking Time: 15 minutes

Servings: 4

Ingredients:

- 2 tablespoons unsalted butter
- 2 medium carrots, cut into ½-inch pieces
- 2 celery stalks, thinly sliced
- 1 small red onion, cut into ¼-inch dice
- 2 garlic cloves, sliced
- 2 cups vegetable broth
- 1 (8-ounce) bottle clam juice
- 1 (10-ounce) can clams
- ½ teaspoon dried thyme
- ½ teaspoon salt
- ¼ teaspoon freshly ground black pepper

Directions:

Dissolve the butter in a large pot, over high heat.

Add the carrots, celery, onion, and garlic and sauté until slightly softened 2 to 3 minutes.

Add the broth and clam juice and boil.

Simmer and cook until the carrots are soft, 3 to 5 minutes.

Stir in the clams and their juices, thyme, salt, and pepper, heat through for 2 to 3 minutes, and serve.

Nutrition:

- Calories: 156
- Total Fat: 7g
- Total Carbohydrates: 7g
- Sugar: 3g
- Fiber: 1g
- Protein: 14g
- Sodium: 981mg

White Bean Chili

Preparation Time: 15 minutes

Cooking Time: 20 minutes

Servings: 4

Ingredients:

- ¼ cup extra-virgin olive oil
- 2 small onions, cut into ¼-inch dice
- 2 celery stalks, thinly sliced
- 2 small carrots, peeled and thinly sliced
- 2 garlic cloves, minced
- 2 teaspoons ground cumin
- 1½ teaspoons dried oregano
- 1 teaspoon salt
- ¼ teaspoon freshly ground black pepper
- 3 cups vegetable broth
- 1 (15½-ounce) can white beans, drained and rinsed
- ¼ finely chopped fresh flat-leaf parsley

- 2 teaspoons grated or minced lemon zest

Directions:

Heat-up the oil over high heat in a Dutch oven.

Add the onions, celery, carrots, and garlic and sauté until softened, 5 to 8 minutes.

Add the cumin, oregano, salt, and pepper and sauté to toast the spices, about 1 minute.

Put the broth and boil.

Simmer, add the beans, and cook, partially covered and occasionally stirring, for 5 minutes to develop the flavors.

Mix in the parsley and lemon zest and serve.

Nutrition:

- Calories: 300
- Total Fat: 15g
- Total Carbohydrates: 32g
- Sugar: 4g
- Fiber: 12g
- Protein: 12g
- Sodium: 1183mg

Layered Greek-Style Vegetables

Preparation Time: 15 minutes

Cooking Time: 50 minutes

Servings: 4

Ingredients:

- ¼ cup extra-virgin olive oil
- 1 medium white onion, thinly sliced
- 2 large zucchinis, thinly sliced
- 2 cups cauliflower florets
- 1 fennel bulb, trimmed and thinly sliced
- 2 garlic cloves, minced
- 1 teaspoon salt
- ¼ teaspoon freshly ground black pepper
- 2 cups vegetable broth
- 1 tablespoon chopped fresh dill
- 1½ teaspoons grated or minced lemon zest
- ½ cup crumbled sheep's or goat's milk feta cheese (optional)

Directions:

Preheat the oven to 400°F.

Pour the oil into a Dutch oven. Put the onion in a single layer, and top, in layers, with the zucchini, cauliflower, fennel, garlic, salt, and pepper.

Put the broth, and sprinkle with the dill and lemon zest.

Cover the pot with the lid, transfer to the oven, and roast until the vegetables are tender, 30 to 40 minutes. Remove, then it let rest for about 10 minutes.

Sprinkle with the feta (if using) and serve.

Nutrition:

- Calories: 200
- Total Fat: 14g
- Total Carbohydrates: 17g
- Sugar: 6g
- Fiber: 6g
- Protein: 7g
- Sodium: 1028mg

Mushroom, Kale, and Sweet Potato Brown Rice

Preparation Time: 10 minutes

Cooking Time: 50 minutes

Servings: 4

Ingredients:

- ¼ cup extra-virgin olive oil
- 4 cups coarsely chopped kale leaves
- 2 leeks, white parts only, thinly sliced
- 1 cup sliced mushrooms
- 2 garlic cloves, minced
- 2 cups peeled sweet potatoes cut into ½-inch dice
- 1 cup of brown rice
- 2 cups vegetable broth
- 1 teaspoon salt
- ¼ teaspoon freshly ground black pepper
- ¼ cup freshly squeezed lemon juice

- 2 tablespoons finely chopped fresh flat-leaf parsley

Directions:

Heat the oil over high heat.

Add the kale, leeks, mushrooms, and garlic and sauté until soft, about 5 minutes.

Add the sweet potatoes and rice and sauté for about 3 minutes.

Add the broth, salt, and pepper and boil. Simmer within 30 to 40 minutes.

Combine in the lemon juice and parsley, then serve.

Nutrition:

- Calories: 425
- Fat: 15g
- Total Carbohydrates: 65g
- Sugar: 6g
- Fiber: 6g
- Protein: 11g
- Sodium: 1045mg

CHAPTER 12:

Snacks and Sides 1

Steamed Broccoli

Preparation Time: 5 minutes

Cooking Time: 1 minute

Servings: 6

Ingredients:

- 6 cups broccoli florets

Directions:

Pour 1½ cups water into the inner pot of the Instant Pot®. Place a steam rack inside.

Place the broccoli florets inside a steamer basket and place the basket on the steam rack.

Steam within 1 minute.

Remove the steamer basket and serve.

Nutrition:

- Calories: 30
- Fat: 0g
- Protein: 3g
- Sodium: 30mg
- Fiber: 2g
- Carbohydrates: 6g
- Sugar: 2g

Boiled Cabbage

Preparation Time: 5 minutes

Cooking Time: 5 minutes

Servings: 6

Ingredients:

- 1 large head green cabbage
- 3 cups vegetable broth
- 1 teaspoon salt
- ½ teaspoon black pepper

Directions:

Place the cabbage, broth, salt, and pepper in the inner pot.

Cook within 5 minutes. Serve.

Nutrition:

- Calories: 54
- Fat: 0g
- Protein: 3g
- Sodium: 321mg
- Fiber: 5g
- Carbohydrates: 13g
- Sugar: 7g

Vegetable "Cheese" Sauce

Preparation Time: 15 minutes

Cooking Time: 11 minutes

Servings: 6

Ingredients:

- 1 small yellow onion, peeled and chopped
- 1 medium zucchini, peeled and sliced
- 6 cloves garlic, chopped
- 2¼ cups vegetable broth, divided
- ¼ teaspoon paprika
- 1 medium sweet potato, peeled and chopped
- ½ cup nutritional yeast

Directions:

Place the onion, zucchini, garlic, and ¼ cup broth into the inner pot. Press the Sauté button and let the vegetables sauté until soft, 5 minutes. Press the Cancel button.

Add the remaining 2 cups broth, paprika, and sweet potato.

Cook within 6 minutes.

Allow to cool for a few minutes and then transfer the mixture to a large blender.

Add the nutritional yeast to the blender with the other ingredients and blend on high until thoroughly combined and smooth.

Serve warm as a topping for the vegetables of your choice.

Nutrition:

- Calories: 58
- Fat: 0g
- Protein: 4g
- Sodium: 226mg
- Fiber: 3g
- Carbohydrates: 10g
- Sugar: 3g

Purple Cabbage Salad with Quinoa and Edamame

Preparation Time: 7 minutes

Cooking Time: 2 minutes

Servings: 8

Ingredients:

- ½ cup dry quinoa
- 1 (10-ounce) bag frozen shelled edamame
- 1 cup vegetable broth
- ¼ cup reduced-sodium tamari
- ¼ cup natural almond butter
- 3 tablespoons toasted sesame seed oil
- ½ teaspoon pure stevia powder
- 1 head purple cabbage, cored and chopped

Directions:

Place the quinoa, edamame, and broth in the inner pot of your Instant Pot. Cook within 2 minutes.

Whisk the tamari, almond butter, sesame seed oil, and stevia in a small bowl. Set aside.

Fluff the quinoa using a fork, and then transfer the mixture to a large bowl. Allow the quinoa and edamame to cool, and then add the purple cabbage to the bowl and toss to combine.

Put the dressing and toss again. Serve.

Nutrition:

- Calories: 220
- Fat: 11g
- Protein: 10g
- Sodium: 313mg
- Fiber: 7g
- Carbohydrates: 21g
- Sugar: 5g

Steamed Cauliflower

Preparation Time: 5 minutes

Cooking Time: 2 minutes

Servings: 6

Ingredients:

- 1 large head cauliflower, cored and cut into large florets

Directions:

Put 2 cups water into the inner pot. Place a steam rack inside.

Place the cauliflower inside a steamer basket and place the basket on the steam rack, steam within 2 minutes.

Carefully remove the steamer basket and serve.

Nutrition:

- Calories: 34
- Fat: 0g
- Protein: 3g
- Sodium: 41mg
- Fiber: 3g
- Carbohydrates: 7g
- Sugar: 3g

Saucy Brussels Sprouts and Carrots

Preparation Time: 15 minutes

Cooking Time: 12 minutes

Servings: 4

Ingredients:

- 1 tablespoon coconut oil
- 12 ounces Brussels sprouts, tough ends removed and cut in half
- 12 ounces carrots (about 4 medium), peeled, ends removed, and cut into 1" chunks
- ¼ cup fresh lime juice
- ¼ cup apple cider vinegar
- ½ cup coconut amino
- ¼ cup almond butter

Directions:

Sauté the Brussels sprouts and carrots and sauté until browned, about 5–7 minutes.

While the vegetables are browning, make the sauce. Mix the lime juice, vinegar, coconut amino, and almond butter in a small bowl.

Pour the sauce over the vegetables—Cook within 6 minutes. Serve.

Nutrition:

- Calories: 216
- Fat: 11g
- Protein: 6g
- Sodium: 738mg
- Fiber: 6g
- Carbohydrates: 22g
- Sugar: 5g

Lemony Cauliflower Rice

Preparation Time: 10 minutes

Cooking Time: 8 minutes

Servings: 4

Ingredients:

- 1 tablespoon avocado oil
- 1 small yellow onion, peeled and diced
- 1 teaspoon minced garlic
- 4 cups riced cauliflower
- Juice from 1 little lemon
- ½ teaspoon salt
- ¼ teaspoon black pepper

Directions:

Put the oil to the pot, and heat 1 minute.

Add the onion and sauté 5 minutes.

Add the garlic and sauté 1 more minute.

Add the cauliflower rice, lemon juice, salt, and pepper and stir to combine—Cook within 1 minute.

Transfer to a bowl for serving.

Nutrition:

- Calories: 60
- Fat: 3g
- Protein: 2g
- Sodium: 311mg
- Fiber: 2g
- Carbohydrates: 6g
- Sugar: 3g

Lemony Steamed Asparagus

Preparation Time: 5 minutes

Cooking Time: 0 minutes

Servings: 4

Ingredients:

- 1-pound asparagus, woody ends removed
- Juice from ½ large lemon
- ¼ teaspoon kosher salt

Directions:

Add ½ cup water to the inner pot and add the steam rack. Add the asparagus to the steamer basket and place the basket on top of the rack, then steam within 1 minute.

Transfer, and top with lemon juice and salt.

Nutrition:

- Calories: 13
- Fat: 0g
- Protein: 1g
- Sodium: 146mg
- Fiber: 1g
- Carbohydrates: 3g
- Sugar: 1g

Lemon Garlic Red Chard

Preparation Time: 10 minutes

Cooking Time: 7 minutes

Servings: 4

Ingredients:

- 1 tablespoon avocado oil
- 1 small yellow onion, peeled and diced
- 1 bunch red chard, leaves and stems chopped and kept separate (about 12 ounces)
- 3 cloves garlic, minced

- ¾ teaspoon salt
- Juice from ½ medium lemon
- 1 teaspoon lemon zest

Directions:

Put the oil to the inner pot and allow it to heat 1 minute. Add the onion and chard stems and sauté 5 minutes. Put the garlic and sauté another 30 seconds. Put the chard leaves, salt, and lemon juice and stir to combine. Turn off. Cook again within 60 seconds.

Scoop the chard mixture into a serving bowl and top with lemon zest.

Nutrition:

- Calories: 57
- Fat: 3g
- Protein: 2g
- Sodium: 617mg
- Fiber: 2g
- Carbohydrates: 6g
- Sugar: 2g

Lemon Ginger Broccoli and Carrots

Preparation Time: 10 minutes

Cooking Time: 5 minutes

Servings: 6

Ingredients:

- 1 tablespoon avocado oil
- 1" fresh ginger, peeled and thinly sliced
- 1 clove garlic, minced
- 2 broccoli crowns, florets
- 2 large carrots, sliced
- ½ teaspoon kosher salt
- Juice from ½ large lemon
- ¼ cup of water

Directions:

Put the oil to the inner pot. Heat-up within 2 minutes.

Add the ginger and garlic and sauté 1 minute. Add the broccoli, carrots, and salt and stir to combine. Turn off.

Add the lemon juice and water and use a wooden spoon to scrape up any brown bits—Cook within 2 minutes.

Serve immediately.

Nutrition:

- Calories: 67
- Fat: 2g
- Protein: 3g
- Sodium: 245mg
- Fiber: 3g
- Carbohydrates: 10g
- Sugar: 3g

Curried Mustard Greens

Preparation Time: 15 minutes

Cooking Time: 10 minutes

Servings: 6

Ingredients:

- 1 tablespoon avocado oil
- 1 medium white onion, peeled and chopped
- 1 tablespoon peeled and chopped ginger
- 3 cloves garlic, minced
- 2 tablespoons curry powder
- ½ teaspoon salt
- ¼ teaspoon black pepper
- 2 cups vegetable broth
- ½ cup coconut cream
- 1 large bunch mustard greens, chopped

Directions:

Add the oil to the inner pot. Press the Sauté button and heat the oil 2 minutes.

Sauté the onion within 5 minutes.

Add the ginger, garlic, curry, salt, and pepper and sauté 1 more minute.

Stir in the vegetable broth and coconut cream until combined and then allow it to come to a boil, about 2–3 minutes more. Turn off.

Stir in the mustard greens until everything is well combined.

Cook within 60 seconds.

Transfer to a bowl and serve.

Nutrition:

- Calories: 124
- Fat: 9g
- Protein: 3g
- Sodium: 388mg
- Fiber: 4g
- Carbohydrates: 9g
- Sugar: 2g

"Cheesy" Brussels Sprouts and Carrots

Preparation Time: 10 minutes

Cooking Time: 10 minutes

Servings: 4

Ingredients:

- 1-pound Brussels sprouts, tough ends removed and cut in half
- 1-pound baby carrots
- 1 cup chicken stock
- 2 tablespoons lemon juice
- ½ cup nutritional yeast
- ¼ teaspoon salt

Directions:

Add the Brussels sprouts, carrots, stock, lemon juice, nutritional yeast, and salt to the inner pot. Stir well to combine. Cook within 10 minutes.

Transfer the vegetables and sauce to a bowl and serve.

Nutrition:

- Calories: 134
- Fat: 1g
- Protein: 9g
- Sodium: 340mg
- Fiber: 8g
- Carbohydrates: 23g
- Sugar: 8g

Garlic Green Beans

Preparation Time: 2 minutes

Cooking Time: 5 minutes

Servings: 4

Ingredients:

- 12 ounces green beans, ends trimmed
- 4 cloves garlic, minced
- 1 tablespoon avocado oil
- ½ teaspoon salt
- 1 cup of water

Directions:

Place the green beans in a medium bowl and toss with the garlic, oil, and salt. Transfer this mixture to the steamer basket.

Put one cup of water into the pot and put the steam rack inside. Place the steamer basket with the green beans on top of the steam rack—Cook within 5 minutes.

Transfer to a bowl for serving.

Nutrition:

- Calories: 58
- Fat: 3g
- Protein: 2g
- Sodium: 295mg
- Fiber: 2g
- Carbohydrates: 6g
- Sugar: 2g

Simple Beet Salad

Preparation Time: 15 minutes

Cooking Time: 5 minutes

Servings: 8

Ingredients:

- 6 medium beets, peeled and cut into small cubes
- 1 cup of water
- ¼ cup extra-virgin olive oil
- ¼ cup apple cider vinegar
- 1 teaspoon Dijon mustard
- ¼ teaspoon pure stevia powder
- ½ teaspoon salt

- ¼ teaspoon black pepper
- 1 large shallot, peeled and diced
- 1 large stalk celery, ends removed and thinly sliced

Directions:

Place the beets into the steamer basket.

Put 1 cup water into the inner pot and place the steam rack inside. Place the steamer basket with the beets on top of the steam rack.

Meanwhile, in a small container or jar with a tight lid, add the oil, vinegar, mustard, stevia, salt, and pepper and shake well to combine. Set aside. Cook within 5 minutes.

Remove, and let the beets cool completely.

Place the shallot and celery in a large bowl and then add the cooked, cooled beets. Serve with the dressing and toss to coat.

Nutrition:

- Calories: 91
- Fat: 7g
- Protein: 1g
- Sodium: 215mg
- Fiber: 2g
- Carbohydrates: 7g
- Sugar: 4g

Cabbage and Avocado Salsa

Preparation Time: 15 minutes

Cooking Time: 12 minutes

Servings: 2

Ingredients:

- ¼ cup veggie stock
- 2 tablespoons olive oil
- 2 spring onions, chopped
- 1 red cabbage head, shredded
- 1 avocado, peeled, pitted, and cubed

Directions:

Add tomatoes and all other ingredients to a suitable cooking pot.

Cover the pot's lid and cook for 12 minutes on medium heat.

Serve fresh and enjoy.

Nutrition:

- Calories 132
- Total Fat 7.1 g
- Sodium 94 mg
- Total Carbs 8.2 g
- Sugar 1.9 g
- Fiber 0.6 g
- Protein 13.5 g

Spinach Cabbage Slaw

Preparation Time: 15 minutes

Cooking Time: 2 minutes

Servings: 2

Ingredients:

- 2 cups red cabbage, shredded
- 1 tablespoon mayonnaise
- 1 spring onion, chopped
- 1-lb. baby spinach
- ½ cup chicken stock

Directions:

Start by adding onion to a suitable pan, to sauté for 2 minutes.

Add spinach, stock and mayonnaise then mix well.

Serve fresh and enjoy.

Nutrition:

- Calories 194
- Total Fat 21.7 g
- Saturated Fat 9.4 g
- Total Carbs 8.3 g
- Sugar 1.6 g
- Fiber 1.3 g
- Protein 3.2 g

Chicken Pesto Salad

Preparation Time: 15 minutes

Cooking Time: 4 minutes

Servings: 2

Ingredients:

- 1-lb. chicken breast, skinless, boneless, and cubed
- 2 tablespoons basil pesto
- 2 tablespoons olive oil
- 2 tablespoons garlic, chopped
- 1 cup tomatoes, crushed

Directions:

Start by adding oil, chicken, and garlic to a cooking pan.

Then sauté for 5 minutes. Stir in pesto and tomatoes.

Cover the pot's lid and cook for 15 minutes on medium heat.

Serve fresh and enjoy.

Nutrition:

- Calories 136
- Total Fat 18.3 g
- Cholesterol 75 mg
- Sodium 104 mg
- Total Carbs 0.6 g
- Sugar 6.2 g
- Fiber 2.9 g
- Protein 5.9 g

Peppers Avocado Salsa

Preparation Time: 15 minutes

Cooking Time: 12 minutes

Servings: 2

Ingredients:

- 1 and ½ lbs. mixed bell peppers, cut into strips
- 1 tablespoon avocado oil
- ½ cup tomato passata
- 1 avocado, peeled, pitted, and cubed
- Salt and black pepper, to taste

Directions:

Add bell peppers and all other ingredients to a suitable cooking pot.

Cover the pot's lid and cook for 12 minutes on medium heat.

Serve fresh and enjoy.

Nutrition:

- Calories 304
- Total Fat 20 g
- Cholesterol 12 mg
- Sodium 645 mg
- Total Carbs 9 g
- Sugar 2 g
- Fiber 5 g
- Protein 22 g

Chard Spread

Preparation Time: 10 minutes

Cooking Time: 15 minutes

Servings: 4

Ingredients:

- 1-lb. salmon fillets, boneless, skinless, and cubed
- Salt and black pepper, to taste
- ¼ lb. Swiss chard, torn
- 1 spring onion, chopped
- ¼ cup chicken stock

Directions:

Add chard with all other ingredients to a cooking pot.

Cover the pot's lid and cook for 15 minutes on medium heat.

Use an immersion blender to blend the spread until smooth.

Serve fresh and enjoy.

Nutrition:

- Calories 294
- Total Fat 16.4 g
- Cholesterol 120 mg
- Sodium 343 mg
- Total Carbs 1.1 g
- Sugar 0.1 g

- Fiber 0.3 g
- Protein 35 g

Olives Coconut Dip

Preparation Time: 5 minutes

Cooking Time: 10 minutes

Servings: 4

Ingredients:

- 4 cups baby spinach
- ½ cup coconut cream
- Salt and black pepper, to taste
- 4 garlic cloves, roasted and minced
- 1 cup kalamata olives, pitted and halved

Directions:

Add olives and all other ingredients to a cooking pot.

Cover the pot's lid and cook for 10 minutes on medium heat.

Use an immersion blender to blend the olives mixture until smooth.

Serve fresh and enjoy.

Nutrition:

- Calories 135
- Total Fat 9.9 g
- Cholesterol 34 mg
- Sodium 10 mg
- Total Carbs 3.1 g
- Sugar 3.4 g
- Fiber 1.5 g
- Protein 8.6 g

Basil Peppers Dip

Preparation Time: 15 minutes

Cooking Time: 15 minutes

Servings: 2

Ingredients:

- 3 shallots, minced
- 1 and ½ lbs. mixed peppers, roughly chopped
- ¼ cup chicken stock
- 1 tablespoon olive oil
- 2 tablespoons basil, chopped

Directions:

Start by sautéing shallots with oil in a pan, then sauté for 2 minutes.

Stir in remaining ingredients and mix well

Cover the pot's lid and cook for 13 minutes on medium heat.

Use an immersion blender to blend the pepper mixture until smooth

Serve fresh and enjoy.

Nutrition:

- Calories 199
- Total Fat 17.4 g
- Cholesterol 47 mg
- Sodium 192 mg
- Total Carbs 9.9 g
- Sugar 1.5 g
- Fiber 4.3 g
- Protein 6.4 g

Watercress Salsa

Preparation Time: 5 minutes

Cooking Time: 12 minutes

Servings: 4

Ingredients:

- 1 bunch watercress, trimmed
- ¼ cup chicken stock
- 1 cup tomato, cubed
- 1 avocado, peeled, pitted, and cubed
- 2 zucchinis, cubed

Directions:

Start by adding watercress and all other ingredients to a cooking pot.

Cover the pot's lid and cook for 10 minutes on medium heat.

Serve fresh and enjoy.

Nutrition:

- Calories 279

- Total Fat 4.8 g
- Cholesterol 45 mg
- Sodium 24 mg
- Total Carbs 5.8 g
- Sugar 2.3 g
- Fiber 4.5 g
- Protein 5 g

Beef Bites

Preparation Time: 10 minutes

Cooking Time: 15 minutes

Servings: 4

Ingredients:

- 1 tablespoon lime juice
- 2 tablespoons avocado oil
- 1-lb. beef stew meat, cubed
- 2 garlic cloves, minced
- 1 cup beef stock

Directions:

Start by adding oil and meat to a cooking pan, then sauté for 5 minutes.

Stir in remaining ingredients and mix well

Cover the pot's lid and cook for 30 minutes on medium heat.

Serve fresh and enjoy.

Nutrition:

- Calories 142
- Total Fat 8.4 g
- Cholesterol 743 mg
- Sodium 346 mg
- Total Carbs 3.4 g
- Sugar 1 g
- Fiber 0.8 g
- Protein 4.1 g

Cheese Stuffed Bell Peppers

Preparation Time: 10 minutes

Cooking Time: 15 minutes

Servings: 4

Ingredients:

- 4 red bell peppers, tops cut off and deseeded
- ¼ cup mozzarella, shredded
- 1 tablespoon garlic, minced
- 2 teaspoons lemon juice
- 1 cup baby spinach, torn

Directions:

To prepare the filling, toss all the ingredients in a bowl except the peppers and water.

Stuff the peppers with the prepared filling.

Place the peppers in a baking sheet and bake for 15 minutes at 375 degrees F.

Serve the peppers and enjoy.

Nutrition:

- Calories 191
- Total Fat 8.4 g
- Cholesterol 743 mg
- Sodium 226 mg
- Total Carbs 7.1 g
- Sugar 0.1 g
- Fiber 1.4 g
- Protein 6.3 g

Olives Parsley Spread

Preparation Time: 10 minutes

Cooking Time: 10 minutes

Servings: 4

Ingredients:

- 2 cups black olives, pitted and halved
- 2 garlic cloves, minced
- 1 tablespoon lemon juice
- 1 tablespoon olive oil
- ¼ cup chicken stock
- Salt and black pepper, to taste

Directions:

Add black olive, chicken stock, and all other ingredients to a suitable cooking pot.

Cover the pot's lid and cook for 10 minutes on medium heat.

Blend this mixture using a handheld blender.

Serve fresh and enjoy.

Nutrition:

- Calories 124
- Total Fat 13.4 g
- Cholesterol 20 mg
- Sodium 136 mg
- Total Carbs 6.4 g
- Sugar 2.1 g
- Fiber 4.8 g
- Protein 4.2 g

Basic Mushroom Salsa

Preparation Time: 10 minutes

Cooking Time: 10 minutes

Servings: 4

Ingredients:

- 1-lb. white mushrooms halved
- ¼ cup chicken stock
- 1 tablespoon basil, chopped
- 2 tomatoes, cubed
- 1 avocado, peeled, pitted, and cubed
- Salt and black pepper, to taste

Directions:

Add mushrooms and all other ingredients to a suitable cooking pot.

Cover the pot's lid and cook for 10 minutes on medium heat.

Serve fresh and enjoy.

Nutrition:

- Calories 104
- Total Fat 3.7 g
- Cholesterol 33 mg
- Sodium 141 mg
- Total Carbs 6.5 g
- Sugar 1.4 g
- Fiber 0.7 g
- Protein 5.4 g

Shrimp with Okra Bowls

Preparation Time: 10 minutes

Cooking Time: 12 minutes

Servings: 4

Ingredients:

- 1-lb. okra, trimmed
- ½ lb. shrimp, peeled and deveined
- 2 tablespoons olive oil
- 1 cup tomato passata, chopped
- 1 tablespoon cilantro, chopped
- Salt and black pepper, to taste

Directions:

Add shrimp, okra, and all other ingredients to a suitable cooking pot.

Cover the pot's lid and cook for 12 minutes on medium heat.

Serve fresh and enjoy.

Nutrition:

- Calories 134
- Total Fat 21.4 g
- Cholesterol 244 mg
- Sodium 10 mg
- Total Carbs 10.1 g
- Sugar 2.7 g
- Fiber 5.2 g
- Protein 2.3 g

Thyme Celery Spread

Preparation Time: 10 minutes

Cooking Time: 12 minutes

Servings: 4

Ingredients:

- 2 lbs. eggplant, roughly chopped
- 2 celery stalks, chopped
- 2 tablespoons olive oil
- 4 garlic cloves, minced

- ½ cup veggie stock
- Salt and black pepper, to taste

Directions:

Stat by adding oil, celery stalks, and garlic to a pan, then sauté for 2 minutes.

Stir in remaining ingredients and mix well

Cover the pot's lid and cook for 10 minutes on medium heat.

Blend the spread using an immersion blender until smooth

Serve fresh and enjoy.

Nutrition:

- Calories 204
- Total Fat 15.7 g
- Cholesterol 49 mg
- Sodium 141 mg
- Total Carbs 12.6 g
- Sugar 3.4 g
- Fiber 1.5 g
- Protein 6.3 g

Nutmeg Spiced Endives

Preparation Time: 10 minutes

Cooking Time: 10 minutes

Servings: 4

Ingredients:

- 4 endives, trimmed and halved
- Salt and black pepper to the taste
- 2 tablespoons olive oil
- 1 teaspoon nutmeg, ground
- 1 tablespoon chives, chopped

Directions:

Toss endives with all other ingredients in a baking sheet.

Bake the endives for 5 minutes in a preheated oven at 350 degrees F.

Serve fresh and enjoy.

Nutrition:

- Calories 131
- Total Fat 10.4 g
- Cholesterol 10 mg
- Sodium 106 mg
- Total Carbs 9.1 g
- Sugar 0.5 g
- Fiber 3.4 g
- Protein 2.3 g

Cucumber-Yogurt Dip

Preparation Time: 15 minutes

Cooking Time: 0 minutes

Servings: 4

Ingredients:

- 1 cucumber, peeled and shredded
- 1 garlic clove, minced
- 2 Tablespoons chopped fresh dill
- 1 teaspoon salt
- 1 cup plain coconut yogurt
- 2 Tablespoons freshly squeezed lemon juice
- 2 Tablespoons extra-virgin olive oil
- 1 scallion, chopped

Directions:

Set down the shredded cucumber in a big sieve to drain.

Take a small bowl and stir together the garlic, salt, yogurt, scallion, dill, and lemon juice.

Fold in the dried cucumber and take to a serving bowl. Before serving, sprinkle with olive oil.

Nutrition:

- Carbohydrate: 7.5g
- Protein: 1.1g
- Total Fat: 9.3g
- Calories: 105
- Cholesterol: 0.0mg
- Fiber: 3.4g

White Bean Dip

Preparation Time: 15 minutes

Cooking Time: 15 minutes

Servings: 4

Ingredients:

- 1 can white beans
- 1 Tablespoon tahini, or almond butter
- ¼ cup chopped pitted green olives
- 1 garlic clove
- 1 Tablespoon chopped fresh parsley
- ¼ Teaspoon salt
- 2 Tablespoons freshly squeezed lemon juice
- 3 Tablespoons extra-virgin olive oil

Directions:

Take a food processor and mix the white beans, garlic, and tahini. With the machine in low-power mode, carefully add the olive oil in a thin, stable stream.

Add the parsley, olives, and salt. Pulse to combine. Pour in the lemon juice. Take to a serving bowl and serve along with raw vegetables

Nutrition:

- Carbohydrate: 26g
- Protein: 9.6g
- Total Fat: 14.2g
- Calories: 240
- Cholesterol: 0.0mg
- Fiber: 6.8g

Mashed Avocado with Jicama Slices

Preparation Time: 15 minutes

Cooking Time: 0 minutes

Servings: 4

Ingredients:

- 2 ripe avocados, pitted
- 1 scallion, sliced
- 2 Tablespoons chopped fresh cilantro
- ½ Teaspoon ground turmeric
- Juice of ½ lemon
- 1 teaspoon salt
- ¼ Teaspoon freshly ground black pepper
- 1 jicama, peeled and cut into ¼-inch-thick slices

Directions:

Take a small bowl and mix the scooped-out avocado, turmeric, the scallion, cilantro, lemon juice, salt, and pepper.

Mash the ingredients together until mixed and still somewhat chunky. Serve along with jicama slices.

Nutrition:

- Carbohydrate: 25g
- Protein: 3.1g
- Total Fat: 20.2g
- Calories: 271
- Cholesterol: 0.0mg
- Fiber: 15.5g

Creamy Broccoli Dip

Preparation Time: 20 minutes

Cooking Time: 5 minutes

Servings: 4

Ingredients:

- 1 cup broccoli florets
- 1 garlic clove
- ½ avocado
- 1 Tablespoon freshly squeezed lemon juice
- 1 teaspoon salt
- ¾ cup unsweetened almond yogurt or coconut yogurt
- ½ Teaspoon dried dill
- Pinch red pepper flakes
- 1 scallion, coarsely chopped

Directions:

Fill two inches of water in a pot, place it over medium flame, and set a steamer basket. Put the broccoli on the steamer basket, cover, and let it steam for five minutes, or until the broccoli attains a bright green hue.

Take off the pan of the flame and drain the broccoli. Take a food processor and add the garlic, avocado, dill, scallion, yogurt, lemon juice, salt, and red pepper flakes.

Pulse a few times until the mixture seems to be chopped. Add the broccoli and process until appropriately blended but not entirely puréed.

Serve along with Sweet Potato Chips or chopped fresh vegetables such as carrots and celery.

Nutrition:

- Carbohydrate: 8g
- Protein: 1g
- Total Fat: 7.4g
- Calories: 83
- Cholesterol: 0.0mg
- Fiber: 4.6g
- Sodium: 629mg

Smoked Trout and Mango Wraps

Preparation Time: 15 minutes

Cooking Time: 0 minutes

Servings: 4

Ingredients:

- 4 ounces smoked trout, divided
- 1 cup chopped mango, divided
- 4 large green-leaf lettuce leaves, thick stems removed
- 1 scallion, sliced, divided
- 2 Tablespoons freshly squeezed lemon juice, divided

Directions:

Find a flat surface and place lettuce leaves on it. Put pieces of trout and mango over each leaf equally.

Dust with the scallions and sprinkle with the lemon juice. Wrap the lettuce leaves in burrito style and set them seam-side down on a serving platter

Nutrition:

- Carbohydrate: 14g
- Protein: 9.2g
- Total Fat: 3.7g
- Calories: 109
- Cholesterol: 0.0mg
- Fiber: 3.5g
- Sodium: 53mg

Kale Chips

Preparation Time: 15 minutes

Cooking Time: 20 minutes

Servings: 4

Ingredients:

- 1 bunch kale, thoroughly washed and dried, ribs detached, and cut into two-inch strips
- 2 Tablespoons extra-virgin olive oil
- 1 teaspoon of sea salt

Directions:

Power on the oven and heat it to 275°F. In a large bowl, bare hands mix the kale and olive oil until the kale gets consistently coated with the oil.

Take the kale to a baking sheet, spreading it in a layer—dust with the sea salt.

Bake within 20 minutes.

Turn the side of the chips halfway through the banking process, so both sides attain the crispiness. Cool the chips a bit before you serve.

Nutrition:

- Carbohydrate: 8g
- Protein: 2.7g
- Total Fat: 7.4g
- Calories: 94
- Cholesterol: 0.0mg
- Fiber: 1.1g
- Sodium: 498mg

Smoked Turkey-Wrapped Zucchini Sticks

Preparation Time: 10 minutes

Cooking Time: 0 minutes

Servings: 4

Ingredients:

- 8 thin slices smoked turkey

- 1 cup packed arugula, divided
- Pinch salt
- 2 zucchinis, quartered lengthwise

Directions:

Place a single slice of smoked turkey on an active working surface. Top with one zucchini stick, one-fourth cup of arugula, and dust of salt.

Wrap the turkey all over the vegetables and lay it on a serving dish seam-side down.

Repeat for the remaining ingredients. Cover and chill until ready to serve.

Nutrition:

- Carbohydrate: 7g
- Protein: 21.7g
- Total Fat: 3.6g
- Calories: 138
- Cholesterol: 0.0mg
- Fiber: 1.2g
- Sodium: 1451mg

Crunchy Chickpeas

Preparation Time: 10 minutes

Cooking Time: 35 minutes

Servings: 1

Ingredients:

- 1 can drained chickpeas (15 ounces)
- ½ Teaspoon ground cumin
- ½ Teaspoon ground turmeric
- ½ Teaspoon chipotle powder
- 1 teaspoon salt
- ¼ Teaspoon garlic powder
- ½ Teaspoon onion powder
- 2 Tablespoons extra-virgin olive oil

Directions:

Power on the oven and heat it to 375°F. Make the drained chickpeas dry using a paper towel.

Mix the salt, chipotle powder, onion powder, cumin, turmeric, and garlic powder in a small bowl.

Take a medium bowl and combine the dry chickpeas and olive oil. Softly stir the chickpeas to place over a coat of oil.

Dust the salt mixture over the chickpeas. Stir the combo till coated evenly.

Take a large baking sheet, raise its sides (to prevent the chickpeas from falling off the sheet), and spread the chickpeas all over layer-wise.

Lay down the sheet in the preheated oven and bake for thirty to forty minutes, stirring in between, or until the chickpeas are dry and crunchy. Cool entirely before eating.

Nutrition:

- Carbohydrate: 19g
- Protein: 8.6g
- Total Fat: 10.4g
- Calories: 193
- Cholesterol: 0.0mg
- Fiber 5.7g
- Sodium: 594mg

Sweet Potato Chips

Preparation Time: 20 minutes

Cooking Time: 2 hours

Servings: 6

Ingredients:

- 3 Tablespoons extra-virgin olive oil
- 1 teaspoon of sea salt
- 2 larges thinly sliced sweet potatoes

Directions:

Power on the oven and heat it to 250°F. Place the rack in the center of the oven.

Take a large bowl and drop in the sweet potatoes' slices along with olive oil. Arrange the slices individually on 2 baking sheets—dust with the sea salt.

Lay the sheets inside the preheated oven and bake for about two hours; make sure to rotate the pans and flip the chips after 45 - 60 minutes.

As soon as the chips turn light brown and attain the crispiness, take them off the oven. Some may be a bit mushy, but they will again turn crisp as they begin to cool.

Let the chips cool for about ten minutes before serving. Serve straight away. The chips will again turn mushy after a few hours.

Nutrition:

- Carbohydrate: 43g
- Protein: 2.7g
- Total Fat: 11.1g
- Calories: 268
- Cholesterol: 0.0mg
- Fiber: 6.5g
- Sodium: 483mg

Mini Snack Muffins

Preparation Time: 20 minutes

Cooking Time: 15 minutes

Servings: 25

Ingredients:

- ¼ cup extra-virgin olive oil
- 1 cup brown rice flour
- 1 cup canned pumpkin
- ¼ Tablespoon olive oil for greasing
- 1 Tablespoon baking powder
- ½ Teaspoon salt
- 1 teaspoon ground cinnamon
- 4 eggs
- 1 cup almond flour
- 1 cup shredded carrot

Directions:

Power on the oven and heat it to 375°F.

With a small brush, line a mini muffin tin with either cupcake liners or little olive oil.

Take a medium bowl and combine the almond flour, baking powder, brown rice flour, salt, and cinnamon.

Add the carrot, eggs, pumpkin, and olive oil. Stir until everything blends properly.

Scoop the batter in each muffin cup, filling each three-quarter only.

Lay the tin inside the preheated oven and bake for fifteen minutes, or until the muffins turn slightly brown.

Take off of the oven and let it cool for ten minutes before removing the muffins from the tin.

Nutrition:

- Carbohydrate: 8g
- Protein: 2.4g
- Total Fat: 4.7g
- Calories: 66
- Cholesterol: 0.0mg
- Fiber: 1.3g
- Sodium: 67mg

Chia - Strawberry Ice Pops

Preparation Time: 5 hours

Cooking Time: 0 minutes

Servings: 6

Ingredients:

- 2 cup frozen unsweetened strawberries, thawed
- 1 (15-ounce) can coconut milk
- 1 Tablespoon chia seeds
- 1 Tablespoon freshly squeezed lemon juice
- 1 teaspoon vanilla extract

Directions:

Arrange six ice pop molds or prepare per the manufacturer's guidelines.

Take a medium bowl and stir together the chia seeds, strawberries, lemon juice, coconut milk, and vanilla.

Allow the mixture to lay still for five minutes, so the chia seeds thicken slightly.

Consistently divide the mixture amongst the molds. Place one ice pop stick in every mold. Freeze the pops for approximately five hours, or overnight. Serve.

Nutrition:

- Carbohydrate: 10g
- Protein: 2.7g
- Total Fat: 17.5g
- Calories: 188
- Cholesterol: 0.0mg
- Fiber: 3.2g

- Sodium: 12mg

Broccoli-Sesame Stir-Fry

Preparation Time: 10 minutes

Cooking Time: 8 minutes

Servings: 4

Ingredients:

- 2 Tablespoons extra-virgin olive oil
- 4 cups broccoli florets
- 2 Tablespoons toasted sesame seeds
- 1 Tablespoon grated fresh ginger
- ¼Teaspoon sea salt
- 1 teaspoon sesame oil
- 2 garlic cloves, minced

Directions:

Heat-up the olive oil and sesame oil in a non-stick pan over medium flame until they start to shimmer.

Now add the broccoli, ginger, and salt. Cook within 7 minutes, frequently stirring, until the broccoli begins attaining a brown hue.

Add the garlic. Cook for thirty seconds, stirring continually.

Take off of the heat and stir the sesame seeds.

Nutrition:

- Carbohydrate: 10.1g
- Protein: 4.6g
- Total Fat: 11.5g
- Calories: 135
- Cholesterol: 0.0mg
- Fiber: 3g
- Sodium: 149mg

Dill and Salmon Pâté

Preparation Time: 15 minutes

Cooking Time: 0 minutes

Servings: 4

Ingredients:

- six ounces cooked salmon, bones and skin removed
- 1 Tablespoon chopped fresh dill
- ½ Teaspoon sea salt
- ¼ cup heavy (whipping) cream

Directions:

Take a blender or a food processor (or instead a large bowl using a mixer), mix the lemon zest, salmon, heavy cream, dill, and salt.

Blend till you attain the proper consistency for the smoothie.

Nutrition:

- Carbohydrate: 0.4g
- Protein; 25.8g
- Total Fat: 12g
- Calories: 199
- Cholesterol: 0.0mg
- Fiber: 0.8g
- Sodium: 296mg

Chickpea - Garlic Hummus

Preparation Time: 6 minutes

Cooking Time: 0 minutes

Servings: 6

Ingredients:

- 3 garlic cloves, minced
- 2 Tablespoons tahini
- 1 can chickpeas, drained
- 2 Tablespoons extra-virgin olive oil
- juice of 1 lemon
- ½ Teaspoon sea salt
- paprika, for garnishing

Directions:

Mix the garlic, tahini, olive oil, chickpeas, lemon juice, and salt in a blender.

Blend till you attain the proper consistency for the snack. Garnish as desired.

Nutrition:

- Carbohydrate: 20.2g
- Protein: 7.3g

- Total Fat: 10.2g
- Calories: 179
- Cholesterol: 0.0mg
- Fiber: 6g
- Sodium: 172mg

Sautéed Apples, Ginger, and Cinnamon

Preparation Time: 10 minutes

Cooking Time: 10 minutes

Servings: 4

Ingredients:

- 2 Tablespoons coconut oil
- 3 apples, peeled and sliced
- 1 teaspoon ground cinnamon
- 1 packet stevia
- 1 Tablespoon grated fresh ginger
- pinch sea salt

Directions:

Heat-up the coconut oil in a non-stick pan over medium flame. Add the apples, cinnamon, ginger, stevia, and salt. Cook for seven to ten minutes, stirring in between until the apples turn mushy.

Nutrition:

- Carbohydrate: 25.1g
- Protein: 0.7g
- Total Fat: 7.6g
- Calories: 151
- Cholesterol: 0.0mg
- Fiber: 5.5g
- Sodium: 61mg

CHAPTER 13:

Snacks and Sides 2

Turmeric Bars

Preparation Time: 2 hours and 5 minutes

Cooking Time: 10 minutes

Servings: 6

Ingredients:

- 1 cup shredded coconut
- 10 dates, pitted
- 1 tablespoon coconut oil
- 1 teaspoon cinnamon
- 1 ¼ cup coconut butter
- 1 ½ teaspoon turmeric powder
- 2 teaspoons honey
- 1/8 teaspoon black pepper

Directions:

Prepare a baking pan and line with parchment paper.

Place the coconut and dates in a food processor and pulse until well-combined. Add in the coconut oil and cinnamon.

Press the dough at the bottom of the pan and set in the fridge for 2 hours.

Make the filling by melting the coconut butter in a double boiler. Stir in turmeric powder and honey.

Pour in the mixture into the pan with the crust.

Chill within 2 hours.

Nutrition:

- Calories 410
- Total Fat 41g
- Total Carbs 13g
- Protein 1g
- Sugar: 11g
- Fiber: 2g
- Sodium: 208mg
- Potassium 347mg

Turmeric Gummies

Preparation Time: 4 hours

Cooking Time: 10 minutes

Servings: 6

Ingredients:

- 1 teaspoon ground turmeric
- 6 tablespoons maple syrup
- 8 tablespoons unflavored gelatin powder
- 3 ½ cups water

Directions:

In a pot, combine the water, turmeric, and maple syrup.

Bring to a boil for 5 minutes.

Remove from the heat and sprinkle with gelatin powder. Mix to hydrate the gelatin.

Turn on the heat and bring to a boil until the gelatin is completely dissolved.

Pour the mixture in a dish and chill the mixture in the fridge for at least 4 hours.

Once set, slice into small squares.

Nutrition:

- Calories 68
- Total Fat 0.03g
- Total Carbs 17g,
- Protein 0.2g
- Sugar: 15g
- Fiber: 0.1g
- Sodium: 19mg
- Potassium 53mg

Ginger Spiced Mixed Nuts

Preparation Time: 5 minutes

Cooking Time: 40 minutes

Servings: 4

Ingredients:

- 2 large egg whites, pasture-raised
- 2 cups mixed nuts (raw almond, pumpkin seeds, cashew, etc.)
- 1 teaspoon grated ginger
- ½ teaspoon salt

Directions:

Preheat the oven to 2500F.

Whip the egg whites until frothy. Add in ginger and salt.

Add in the mixed nuts into the egg mixture. Stir to coat everything.

Spread the nuts evenly on to the baking sheet.

Bake for 40 minutes.

Allow the mixture to cool and harden.

Cut into pieces, then store in the fridge until ready to consume

Nutrition:

- Calories 423
- Total Fat 36g
- Total Carbs 16g
- Protein 17g
- Sugar: 3g
- Fiber: 9g
- Sodium: 28mg
- Potassium 553mg

Spicy Tuna Rolls

Preparation Time: 10 minutes

Cooking Time: 0 minutes

Servings: 6

Ingredients:

- 1 medium cucumber
- 1 can yellowfin tuna, wild-caught
- 2 slices avocado, diced
- 1/8 teaspoon salt
- 1/8 teaspoon pepper

Directions:

Thinly slice the cucumber lengthwise.

Combine the tuna and avocado in a mixing bowl—season with salt and pepper to taste.

Spoon the tuna and avocado mixture and spread evenly on cucumber slices.

Roll the cucumber slices and secure the ends with toothpicks.

Chill before serving.

Nutrition:

- Calories 135
- Total Fat 10g
- Total Carbs 6g
- Protein 7g
- Sugar:0.9 g
- Fiber: 5g
- Sodium: 73mg
- Potassium 420mg

Veggie Burrito

Preparation Time: 10 minutes

Cooking Time: 5 minutes

Servings: 2

Ingredients:

- 4 medium collard greens, stalks trimmed
- 1 teaspoon avocado oil
- 1/3 cup bell pepper, julienned
- 1/3 cup chopped tomatoes
- 1/3 cup red onions, sliced thinly
- ¼ cup avocado meat
- 1 cup cooked quinoa
- ¼ cup cilantro leaves, chopped
- ¼ teaspoon salt

Directions:

Boil water, and blanch the collard greens. Set aside.

Heat-up the avocado oil over medium flame in a skillet and sauté the bell pepper for 1 minute. Set aside.

Assemble the burrito by placing the blanched collard greens on a flat surface.

Place the bell pepper, tomatoes, onions, avocado meat, and quinoa in the center. Add in the cilantro leaves.

Roll the collard greens to create a burrito.

Nutrition:

- Calories 175
- Total Fat 7g
- Total Carbs 25g
- Net Carbs 20g
- Protein 5g
- Sugar: 3g
- Fiber: 5g
- Sodium:11 mg
- Potassium 372mg

Spicy Kale Chips

Preparation Time: 10 minutes

Cooking Time: 20 minutes

Servings: 4

Ingredients:

- 1 bunch curly kale, rinsed
- ¼ teaspoon ground cayenne pepper
- 1/8 teaspoon garlic powder
- spray oil for greasing
- ¼ teaspoon salt
- 1/8 teaspoon black pepper

Directions:

Preheat the oven to 3000F.

Pat dry the kale to remove water.

Tear the kale leaves into pieces, then place on a baking sheet lined with foil.

Spray with cooking oil and season with garlic powder, season, and black pepper.

Bake within 20 minutes. Serve.

Nutrition:

- Calories 5
- Total Fat 0.08g
- Total Carbs 1g
- Protein 0.4g
- Sugar: 0.3g
- Fiber: 0.3g
- Sodium: 3mg
- Potassium 50mg

Ginger Date Bars

Preparation Time: 10 minutes

Cooking Time: 20 minutes

Servings: 8

Ingredients:

- 1 ½ cups almond, soaked in water overnight, then drained
- ¾ cup dates pitted
- ¼ cup almond milk
- 1 teaspoon ground ginger

Directions:

Preheat the oven to 3500F.

Place the almond in a food processor. Pulse to form a thick dough.

Press the dough in a baking dish lined with parchment paper. Set aside.

For the date mix, combine the rest of the ingredients in a food processor. Pulse until smooth.

Pour the date mixture on to the almond crust. Bake for 20 minutes. Allow cooling before slicing.

Nutrition:

- Calories 45
- Total Fat 0.3g
- Total Carbs 11g
- Protein 0.5g
- Sugar: 9g
- Fiber: 1g
- Sodium: 6mg
- Potassium 101mg

Vanilla Turmeric Orange Juice

Preparation Time: 2 hours

Cooking Time: 0 minutes

Servings: 2

Ingredients:

- 3 oranges, peeled and quartered
- 1 cup almond milk, unsweetened
- 1 teaspoon vanilla extract
- ½ teaspoon cinnamon
- ¼ teaspoon turmeric
- a pinch of pepper

Directions:

Place all ingredients in a blender. Pulse until smooth.

Put into glasses, then chill in the fridge before serving.

Nutrition:

- Calories 188
- Total Fat 5g
- Total Carbs 33g
- Protein 5g
- Sugar: 27g
- Fiber: 6g
- Sodium: 53mg

Hibiscus Ginger Gelatin

Preparation Time: 2 hours

Cooking Time: 20 minutes

Servings: 5

Ingredients:

- 3 tablespoons dried hibiscus flower
- 1 ½ tablespoon honey
- 1 teaspoon ginger juice
- 2 tablespoons gelatin powder
- 1 cup of water

Directions:

Boil water, remove, then add the hibiscus flowers. Allow infusing for 5 minutes.

Remove the flowers and discard them. Heat the liquid and add the honey, ginger, and gelatin.

Allow the gelatin to dissolve. Pour the mixture into a baking sheet.

Chill, and allow to set. Slice the gelatin once it hardens.

Nutrition:

- Calories 27
- Total Fat 0.06g
- Total Carbs 7g
- Protein 0.2g
- Sugar: 7g
- Fiber: 0g

Turmeric Nuggets

Preparation Time: 15 minutes

Cooking Time: 25 minutes

Servings: 4

Ingredients:

- 2 cups cauliflower florets
- 2 cups broccoli florets
- 1 cup carrots, chopped
- 1 teaspoon garlic, minced
- ½ teaspoon ground turmeric
- ½ cup almond meal
- 2 egg, pasture-raised
- ¼ teaspoon salt
- ¼ teaspoon black pepper

Directions:

Preheat the oven to 4000F and line a baking sheet with parchment paper.

Pulse all fixings in a food processor until smooth.

Scoop a tablespoon of mixture and place on the baking sheet.

Bake for 25 minutes.

Nutrition:

- Calories 97
- Total Fat 5g
- Total Carbs 7g
- Protein 7g
- Sugar: 3g
- Fiber: 3g

Coconut Flour Muffins

Preparation Time: 10 minutes

Cooking Time: 25 minutes

Servings: 6

Ingredients:

- 6 large eggs, pasture-raised
- ½ cup unsweetened coconut milk
- 1/3 cup maple syrup
- 1 teaspoon vanilla extract
- ¾ cup + 2 tablespoons coconut flour
- ½ teaspoon baking soda
- 2 teaspoon turmeric powder
- ½ teaspoon ginger powder
- salt and pepper to taste

Directions:

Preheat the oven to 3500F.

Combine the eggs, milk, maple syrup, and vanilla in a mixing bowl.

In another bowl, sift the coconut flour, baking soda, turmeric, and ginger powder—season with salt and pepper to taste.

Pour the wet fixings into the dry fixings until well-combined.

Pour into the prepared muffin tins. Bake within 25 minutes. Serve.

Nutrition:

- Calories 157
- Total Fat 9g
- Total Carbs 15g
- Protein 3g
- Sugar: 12g
- Fiber: 1g

No-Bake Golden Energy Bites

Preparation Time: 60 minutes

Cooking Time: 0 minutes

Servings: 16

Ingredients:

- 1 cup almond butter
- ¾ cup coconut flakes, unsweetened
- 6 tablespoons protein powder
- 1 teaspoon coconut oil
- ½ teaspoon maple syrup
- 2 teaspoons turmeric

Directions:

Combine all fixings until a thick dough is formed in a bowl.

Place dough in a pan lined with parchment paper and spread evenly.

Chill within an hour to set. Remove, then slice to 16 pieces.

Nutrition:

- Calories 376
- Total Fat 36g
- Saturated Fat 5g
- Total Carbs 9g
- Protein 6g
- Sugar: 5g
- Fiber: 2g

Banana Ginger Bars

Preparation Time: 10 minutes

Cooking Time: 40 minutes

Servings: 5

Ingredients:

- 2 large ripe bananas, peeled and mashed
- 1 cup coconut flour
- 1/3 cup coconut oil
- 1/3 cup raw honey
- 6 eggs, pasture-raised
- 1 tablespoon grated fresh ginger
- 2 teaspoons cinnamon powder
- 1 teaspoon ground cardamom powder
- 1 teaspoon baking soda
- 2 teaspoons apples cider vinegar

Directions:

Preheat the oven to 3500F. Grease a baking dish.

Combine the bananas, coconut flour, coconut oil, honey, eggs, ginger, cinnamon, and cardamom in a food processor. Pulse until smooth.

Put the baking soda plus apple cider vinegar last and quickly blend.

Pour into the prepared pan. Bake within 40 minutes. Allow cooling before slicing.

Nutrition:

- Calories 364
- Total Fat 26g
- Total Carbs 23g
- Protein 12g
- Sugar: 20g
- Fiber: 1g

Kombucha Gummies

Preparation Time: 3 hours

Cooking Time: 10 minutes

Servings: 5

Ingredients:

- 1 teaspoon grated ginger
- 1 ½ cups plain kombucha
- ½ cup of grapefruit juice
- 1 tablespoon grapefruit zest
- 6 tablespoons honey
- 1/3 cup gelatin powder

Directions:

Line the bottom of a glass pan with plastic wrap. Set aside.

In a pot, add the ginger and a cup of water. Bring to a boil for 5 minutes. Drain and save the grated ginger.

In another saucepan, combine the kombucha, grapefruit juice, zest, and honey. Sprinkle with the gelatin powder and allow to hydrate for 5 minutes.

Turn on the heat and bring to a boil until the gelatin dissolves. Add in the grated ginger.

Pour into the mixture the prepared glass and chill for 3 hours until the gelatin has set.

Slice into small squares.

Nutrition:

- Calories 99
- Total Fat 0.03g
- Total Carbs 26g
- Protein 0.4g
- Sugar: 26g
- Fiber: 0.1g

Cacao Coffee Protein Bars

Preparation Time: 10 minutes

Cooking Time: 0 minutes

Servings: 6

Ingredients:

- 2 cups mixed nuts (almond, pecans, cashew, and walnuts
- 1 cup egg white protein powder
- ¼ cup cacao powder
- 3 tablespoons powdered coffee
- 18 large Medjool dates, pitted
- ¼ cup raw cacao nibs
- 5 tablespoons water

Directions:

Line a baking pan with parchment paper. Set aside

In a food processor, pulse the nuts, protein powder, cacao powder, and powdered coffee.

Add in the pitted dates and process until fine crumbs form. If dry, add a tablespoon of water until a sticky dough is formed.

Place in a bowl and stir in the cacao nibs. Spread the batter into the pan. Chill within 30 minutes before slicing.

Nutrition:

- Calories 493
- Total Fat 25g
- Total Carbs 67g
- Protein 12g
- Sugar: 50g
- Fiber: 12g

Conclusion

Starting an anti-inflammatory diet can be difficult. There are many rules to follow, foods to avoid, and advice to follow. That's what makes it so successful, though! It helps you get rid of the wrong foods for you and ensures that you will give your body the good stuff by eliminating the wrong thing; all in the hope of reducing the amount of inflammation and the adverse health effects in your body.

As a beginner, you may be a little confused about how to start with this diet plan. But don't let this stop you! There are tips below to help you be sure you can get the most out of your anti-inflammatory diet!

Find A Friend to Do the Diet with You

You will want to consider when it is time to get started on the anti-inflammatory diet is whether you can find a friend who is willing to do this with you. Doing this diet plan, or any kind of diet plan, on your own, can be tedious and challenging. When you notice some people around you getting eat and enjoy what they want and focus on only eating certain foods, it is challenging to stay on this diet plan. And if you were recently an unhealthy person who didn't eat well and didn't exercise hardly at all, this will become even more difficult.

Having a friend who can work with you on this, and who will keep you on track, is going to make a big difference. You can both share recipes, talk through things when it feels hard, and provide each other with the support needed to feel your best.

Look for Some Good Recipes

When you take a look through the anti-inflammatory diet, you likely see a lot of information about the foods you need to avoid. The list will seem long and scary, and your mind may blank on ideas for meals to make with what you have.

There are many great meals and foods that you can enjoy when you go on this diet plan. But since our minds are going to focus most on the foods that we are not allowed to have, rather than all of the right foods that we can enjoy, we will lose focus, panic, and have trouble.

Finding some good recipes, like those you will discover inside this guidebook, will make a big difference. These can help you pick out the delicious meals needed to keep you healthy and feel your very best in the process. Take a look at the meal plan and the recipes that we have at the end of this book and see why following this diet plan will be so delicious and so much easier than you could have imagined in the long run.

Come Up with Some Motivation to Help You Stay on Track

Following the idea of the anti-inflammatory diet can be challenging. If you are not careful and don't have a fair amount of motivation to help you out with this one, it will be even harder to see the results you would like.

Finding a good motivator from the start will keep you alive and allow you to see the results you want can make everything easier. Think about why you want to follow this dietary plan. Why is it so crucial to get results on this dietary plan and see the results you want?

Wanted to lose weight? Do you feel much pain throughout your body and want to control it as much as possible? Are you interested in cutting out some of the health problems that come with inflammation? Are you tired of feeling lazy and exhausted all the time and want to keep up and play with your children regularly? Or is there any other reason you cannot enjoy things as you would like and want to use it as a personal motivation for the long term?

Each person will have their motivation, desire to work hard, and follow the anti-inflammatory diet. And that's fine. You need to understand what works best for you and then regularly see it in a place you can see. This way, you will take care of yourself and not give up on the anti-inflammatory diet, even when things start to get complicated.

Eating on the Anti-Inflammatory Diet

The foods you follow on this diet are different from what you can do with other diet plans. It is because it is necessary to focus on the need to avoid foods that cause inflammation. And you need to consume many foods that can limit the amount of inflammation found in the body.

You will want to stay with healthy whole grains, lean meats that contain many healthy fats, such as fish, healthy fats, and many fresh products. When you can combine all these things well together, you will find that it is much easier to see the health benefits and reduce inflammation to the limit. Let's now outline a few rules that you can do to help you get the most out of your food in this diet plan:

Aim to get a lot of variety into your diet. It will not be entertaining to go on this diet plan and only eat a few products each day or the same meals. Sure, this will make things more comfortable because you don't need to think them through. But it won't be long before you are bored. Try to switch out the foods you eat and add as much color to each plate you eat. It will help you not get bored and ensure that your body will get all of the healthy nutrients that it needs. It's a healthy game, have fun!

Add fresh food. If you are still eating junk and processed foods, you will not do well on this diet plan. Your foods should be fresh and wholesome as much as possible. If you can try to stay in the outer aisles at the grocery store, you should be good;

Cut out the fast foods and processed foods. These will be full of all the harmful nutrients that you do not want to have, and they are going to cause inflammation. If you have taken the time to be on this diet, you go and eat a bit of processed food; you will notice it right away. Discourage this as much as you can, and eat at home to help you stay healthy and get the best of this diet;

Eat lots of fruits. This diet plan asks you to take some time to add more fruits and vegetables to your meals. It will give you the nutrients that your body needs, and they help eliminate some of the toxins and free radicals that are going to cause the inflammation that you need to be able to watch out for.

Try the Elimination Diet

When working with your anti-inflammatory diet, you may want to spend some time looking at the elimination diet. It is an easy idea to focus on and ensure that you can reduce all of the foods causing inflammation in the body.

The idea with this one is that some foods are more likely to cause inflammation, but they don't cause inflammation in each person who eats them. Sometimes you will be fine eating these foods, and other times you will need to stop eating them to reduce the inflammation. You will do the elimination diet to figure out whether or not this is the issue for you or not.

To make this work, you want to eliminate all of the foods that we have been talking about in this guidebook, which are seen as inflammation-causing. But then, we need to cut out a few other options as well. Often, you will need to remove things that have gluten and dairy in them. If you feel that other options could be causing the inflammation for you, also eliminate them.

Spend a few weeks following the anti-inflammatory diet, along with this elimination diet, and see how you feel. You should see that your energy levels are up, you don't feel as bloated regularly any longer, and your mood improves. You may not have noticed how badly you felt up until this point. And that is just fine. It is an excellent encouragement that will ensure you stick with this diet plan.

Then, afterward, it is time to start re-introducing these foods back into your diet. Just do one food, or one food group at a time, and see how it works for you. If you can introduce food back into the diet and don't notice your health goes downhill, and you don't start to see a decrease in how you feel, it is fair to eat that anti-inflammatory food diet. You will find that the foods you can eat at this time are not causing any sensitivity to you, and they are perfectly safe for you.

But, if you decide to try the food again and then feel sick, have bloating, have a headache, or something else seems to be off with this, you know that you have a sensitivity to it. That means you need to cut the food out and not focus on eating them at all. They cause a lot of inflammation in your body, even though they may not harm someone else, and taking the time to cut them out will make a big difference in how good you feel.

There are many ways to enhance your body health with the help of the anti-inflammatory diet. It is a simple idea meant to improve so many aspects of your health by reducing inflammation in your body. If you can follow the guidelines that come with it and stick with some of the tips above, then you are sure to see a massive difference in your whole health.

Printed in the USA
CPSIA information can be obtained
at www.ICGtesting.com
LVHW082316150824
788423LV00029B/911